# MINING SITES IN CORNWALL
# & SOUTH WEST DEVON

# MINING SITES
# IN CORNWALL &
# SOUTH WEST DEVON

**by**

**Barry Atkinson**

*NOV. 1995.*

DYLLANSOW
TRURAN

First published 1988 by Dyllansow Truran, 'Trewolsta', Trewirgie, Redruth, Kernow.

ISBN No. 185 022 044 1

Typeset and printed by St. George Printing Works Ltd, Commercial Centre, Wilson Way, Pool Industrial Estate, Redruth, Cornwall

# Abbreviations

Name of Mine — alternative title in brackets
D.     Chief periods of operation
L.     Location with Grid Reference number — $2\frac{1}{2}''$ O/S
M/O.  Mineral Output
S.     The site as it appears today
Dir.   Directions to a particularly difficult location
Note.  Small 'and' between names indicates two separate mines that eventually worked together.

# Contents

# Introduction

This book can best be described as a layman's guide for the budding industrial archaeologist or anyone whose interest and curiosity has been aroused by the numerous and often striking remains of former mining activity still to be seen in Cornwall and parts of Devon. I do not propose dwelling on the history of these mines — other books are readily available on that aspect of the industry. The aim is to provide a name and a route to a particular location, and a description of what can be viewed today.

Up until the end of the 1960's there existed, especially in West Cornwall, large tracts of derelict mining ground that had lain almost undisturbed for over a century. Since the end of that decade, the developers have moved in and in many areas the country has been 'cleaned up'. Housing estates have mushroomed over long abandoned workings, new roads plough through once prosperous mining fields, dumps have been levelled and engine houses and stacks have been bulldozed for no other reason than to erect a new bungalow, despite local protest. It was this worrying trend of destroying what was, after all, part of Cornwall's industrial heritage that led the writer to undertake to visit, catalogue and photograph every known site in the region on which some form of mining relic was still existent. Over the ensuing years, numerous excursions in Cornwall and Devon showed that some of the better known mining remains were showing signs of depredation, whilst many of the several hundred or so smaller prospects researched by Dr. A. K. Hamilton Jenkin in his classic series 'The Mines and Miners of Cornwall' were no longer visible and had been lost forever. Enough remains at surface, however, to be detailed in this volume.

The sites visited have been grouped into localities rather than alphabetical order and the Devon side of the Tamar around Tavistock is included because of the close proximity and association of the mines along both sides of the river. Many abandoned mining setts are on farmland and, in some cases, private property. Permission should therefore be sought, usually from the local farmer, to visit — and obviously caution is needed when exploring these workings. A great deal of footwork is required to locate those mines that are situated well off the beaten track and therefore not easy to reach by more conventional means.

Included are buildings, usually the ubiquitous engine house, that have fallen over the past few years, either by the hand of man or by natural forces. Detailed directions to the more inaccessible mines are given, and the whole text is in straightforward, non-technical terms.

# List of Plates

# Bibliography

'Mines & Miners of Cornwall' Volumes 1-16        Dr. A.K. Hamilton Jenkin

'The Metalliferous Mining Region of South
    West England' Volumes 1 & 2                   H.G. Dines

'Cornish Engine Houses' Volumes 1 & 2            H.G. Ordish

'Industrial Archaeology of the Tamar Valley'     Frank Booker

'Mines of Devon' Volume 1                        Dr. A.K. Hamilton Jenkin

'Wendron Tin'                                    Dr. A.K. Hamilton Jenkin

'A History of Tin Mining & Smelting in
    Cornwall'                                    D.B. Barton

# St. Just — St. Ives

## WHEAL HERMON (LETCHA CLIFF MINE)

D.   1835–1891, 1912–1919
L.   $\frac{3}{4}$ mile SW of St. Just SW356306
M/O.   Only 6 tons of tin recorded
S.   Cavernous workings and levels between Letcha Cliff and Gribba Point. Three adit portals are adjacent to the cliff footpath, together with the granite masonry of a water wheel pit. Several shafts, still open, are to be found at the top of Hermon Hill and Carn Laskys.

## COT VALLEY

L.   $\frac{1}{2}$ mile SW of St. Just SW362305
M/O.   No records — the valley was used for tin streaming and the treatment of ore from the surrounding mines, on a small scale.
S.   Two ruined buildings used for ore dressing lie in dense undergrowth near Lower Bosavern at the head of the valley. The entrances of at least six levels can be located on either side of the track leading to Porth Nanven, with remains of an old dressing plant and traces of buddles near the boulder strewn beach.

## ST. JUST UNITED and
## ST. JUST AMALGAMATED

D.   1862–1904
L.   $\frac{3}{4}$ mile W of St. Just SW354313–SW353315
M/O.   2,982 tons tin
S.   An imposing chimney stack adorns the cliff top at Bollowall, standing near the antiquity known as Carn Gloose. Main engine shaft, surrounded by a square granite collar, is on the verge of the cliff overlooking both Priest Cove and Cape Cornwall, which still exhibits the small stack of Cape Cornwall Mine.

## BOSCEAN

D.   1837–1865
L.   $\frac{1}{2}$ mile NW of St. Just SW363322
M/O.   2,400 tons tin
S.   A small, well preserved chimney stack overlooks the Nancherrow Valley, directly opposite the engine house of Wheal

Drea, together with a sizeable dump. Main adit adjoins the footpath leading down into the valley. The remains of the count house also exist on the site.

## BALLESWIDDEN and EAST BALLESWIDDEN

D.    1833–1894, re-worked 1913–1916
L.    1 mile E of St. Just SW387311
M/O.  11,900 tons tin
S.    Two chimney stacks standing on Lafrowda Common can be seen near the road from St. Just to Newbridge, together with the concrete remains of a dressing plant dating from the last period of working. East Balleswidden's sett is also marked by a single stack by the road to Dowran.

## BOSWEDDEN and NANCHERROW VALLEY

D.    1837–1876
L.    1 mile NW of St. Just SW357323
M/O.  1,375 tons tin; 200 tons copper; 75 tons haematite
S.    Most of this mine was destroyed by a cloudburst that swept through the valley in 1902. Several adits, dangerous to enter, are still open and the cliffs here are scarred with old men's workings. Part of the stamps engine house and stack remains, at the seaward end of the valley. Nearby are the massive walls constructed of dressed granite blocks that supported one of the mine's two waterwheels. A large dressing plant was erected in the Nancherrow Valley at SW360324 — the various buildings, now much overgrown with vegetation, still remain with their distinctive tall stack crowned with ornamental brickwork.

## WHEAL OWLES (WHEAL EDWARD)

D.    1821–1907
L.    ¾ mile NW of St. Just SW362327
M/O.  8,950 tons tin; 2,079 tons copper; 50 tons arsenic; 5 cwt uranium
S.    Wheal Owles exploited a large tract of land, from Kenidjack Cliff to Truthwall, and as a result the whole area is littered with abandoned engine houses, shafts and dumps. The lane leading from Truthwall to the cliffs, near the B3306 road at Tregeseal, passes Wheal Boys section, where the crumbling bob-wall of one engine house and the base walls of another are perched on the

edge of an extremely deep and cavernous shaft. The small engine house and count house at Kenidjack hamlet marks the site of Wheal Drea, opposite Boscean Mine. A substantial part of another engine house stands amidst tons of granite and waste rock at SW365324. Wheal Edward's stamps and pumping engine houses form a fine pair on the rugged cliffs overlooking Wheal Edward Zawn, although both buildings are now in a state of disrepair.

## THE BUNNY
L.     1 mile N of St. Just SW364333

S.     A series of excavations, caverns and tunnels with various openings on either side of the coastal footpath, probably the site of the original Botallack workings dating back to the early years of the 19th century. These are comparitively safe to explore as the average length of the passages is short, although some of the openings have been partly obscured by rubble as a result of the Geevor re-opening of Allen's Shaft.

Plate 1: *Botallack — engine houses at Crowns*

3

## BOTALLACK

D. 1815–1914
L. 1 mile N of St. Just SW365331
M/O. 22,465 tons copper; 14,888 tons tin; 1,525 tons arsenic
S. The best known industrial relics in Cornwall are the pumping and whim engine houses poised on the steep cliffs at the Crowns, restored in 1984/5. A truncated stack stands above the whim, formerly connected by a flue. Two stacks, concrete buddles and dressing floors can be found in the vicinity of Allen's Shaft. At SW363338, the Wheal Cock section of the mine, are two brick-lined shafts leading to the submarine levels, each encircled by a granite collar.

## LEVANT

D. 1820–1930
L. 2 miles N of St. Just SW370345
M/O. 130,000 tons copper; 24,000 tons tin; 4,000 tons arsenic
S. The whole area from Roscommon to Trewellard Bottoms is virtually one vast dressing floor complex, with piles of rubble, ruined furnaces, empty treatment ponds and blackened calciners. The stack of the ill-fated man engine survives, but the building itself is nothing more than a pile of stone, and the shaft is a rubbish filled depression. The timbered level which connects to this shaft has its portal adjacent to the coast footpath. The 24″ whim, engine 'in situ', and 70″ pumping engine houses on Skip Shaft are in good condition, but only a fractional part of the stamps engine house survives near an attendant stack. There is a wooden headframe over one of the Levant's submarine levels on the verge of the cliff near Levant Zawn. Extensive treatment ponds and wooden launders are to be seen at Trewellard Bottoms, where the sea is stained a muddy red with the discharge from both Levant and Geevor. A distinctive red-bricked stack stands attached to the remains of the compressor house, and the calciners left from arsenic production are amongst the most impressive in Cornwall.

## HIGHER BAL

L. 1½ miles N of St. Just SW369342
M/O. Included with Levant
S. A well preserved whim engine house with attendant masonry

4

standing beside Levant Road, the last such building to utilise a wooden head frame in the county. The shaft has been capped for safety, and access to this was formerly made by a flight of granite steps that run underneath the road.

## SPEARN CONSOLS and SPEARN MOOR
D.   1811–1878
L.   1½ miles N of St. Just SW373334–SW373338
M/O.   2,800 tons tin; 315 tons copper; some arsenic
S.   Two closely related setts situated on the rather featureless stretch of moorland west of Carnyorth. Apart from vast heaps of 'deads', a single stack and the ruins of an old dry stand on the sett. Near Levant Road are the remains of a small engine house, with wooden lintels intact in the window opening. Also of interest, but hard to find amidst all the rubble, is a small shaft lined with granite blocks, on the eastern part of the property.

## NORTH LEVANT
D.   1852–1891
L.   2 miles NE of St. Just SW375340
M/O.   Small amounts of tin and copper
S.   The base walls of an engine house and stack are situated near the lane from Trewellard to Lower Boscaswell. This relic was unearthed in 1982 when men employed by Geevor were clearing and levelling old dumps in the area. With no shaft visible in the vicinity, the building was used either for stamping or winding. At SW373341 is a series of small levels at the edge of a field, where mining was carried out at a shallow depth.

## PENDEEN CONSOLS
D.   1858–1870, re-worked 1907–1918
L.   2¾ miles NE of St. Just SW382358
M/O.   6,860 tons copper; 146 tons tin
S.   The roofless count house of this small copper producer stands on Pendeen Cliff overlooking the lighthouse, together with a fenced shaft and a few scattered dumps.

## BOSCASWELL DOWNS
D.   1837–1912
L.   2¼ miles NE of St. Just SW382345

M/O.　1,295 tons tin; 700 tons copper

S.　Very extensive workings covering the area from Pendeen Village to Lower Boscaswell. Pumping engine house on Engine Shaft, with a cottage built onto the side wall, adjoins the B3306 St. Just road at SW384344. In a nearby clump of thickets are the base walls of the whim. A small stack formerly connected to this whim stands in a private garden a short distance down the road to Lower Boscaswell. At SW381350, the site of the Trease operations is marked by a single stack and the remains of a dressing plant. A headgear over Trease Shaft dominates the village, this now forming part of the Geevor workings.

## WHEAL HEARLE (EAST BOSCASWELL)

D.　1861–1875

L.　½ mile E of Pendeen SW391339

M/O.　275 tons tin; 70 tons copper

S.　The well preserved pumping and whim engine houses of this small mine stand on Portheras Common beside the B3318 Penzance road.

## OXMAN'S STAMPS

L.　1 mile NE of Pendeen SW390355

S.　Practically the whole length of the Portheras Valley was utilised by the surrounding mines for tin streaming and ore dressing. The buildings remaining from these operations, some of considerable size, which housed the stamps and water wheels, are now in ruins and partly hidden by encroaching undergrowth, although fairly accessible. The valley is best approached by taking the path from Rose Valley to Portheras Cove.

## MORVAH CONSOLS

D.　1851–1874

L.　½ mile NE of Morvah Church SW407359

M/O.　6 tons tin

S.　The crumbling remains of the small pumping engine house, shaft and a few walls stand on Morvah Cliff. Slightly north east is another building on the valley side, possibly an old dry.

## GARDEN MINE

D.　1838–1870

L.    1 mile E of Morvah SW417356

M/O.  A few tons of tin

S.    Three walls of the pumping engine house and a fenced shaft survive on the mist-shrouded summit of Watchcroft, whose bracken-covered slopes are riddled with levels, small quarries and shafts. Caution is therefore required when negotiating the hill to view this mine.

## CARN GALVER (ROSEMERGY)

D.    1870–1876

L.    1½ miles NE of Morvah SW421364

M/O.  150 tons tin

S.    Restored in 1984, the pumping and whim engine houses of this small tin mine stand beside the St. Ives–St. Just coastal road, below Watchcroft. At Porthmeor Valley, SW430371, are the remains of a small dressing plant comprising two buildings and a chimney stack, used by the Morvah Consols Group for the treatment of tin.

## GURNARD'S HEAD MINE

D.    1821–1847

L.    2 miles N of Morvah SW437382

M/O.  25 tons copper

S.    A small ruinous pumping engine house and shaft are on the verge of the cliff overlooking the headland of the same name. This is quite difficult to reach — the cliffs here are swampy, overgrown and intersected by numerous streams.

## CARNELLOE (ZENNOR CONSOLS)

D.    1852–1876

L.    ¾ mile NW of Zennor SW444388

M/O.  6 tons tin

S.    The shafts, dumps and adits of this unproductive tin producer litter the cliff top between Porthglaze and Veor Coves.

## TREVEGA BAL (BREA CONSOLS)

D.    1826–1865

L.    2 miles NE of Zennor SW482405

M/O.  75 tons tin

S.    Part of the stamps engine house stands prominently on the cliff

## DING DONG

D.    1815–1878
L.    2¼ miles E of Morvah SW436344
M/O.  3,475 tons tin
S.    The pumping engine house on the granite-walled Greenburrow Shaft is a landmark for miles on the high moors north of Penzance. The lane to Tredinnick passes the whim engine house and smaller stamps, both in good condition. This area abounds in un-fenced shafts hidden by bracken, so care must be taken when one is in the vicinity of this mine.

## NANJIZAL (MILL) BAY

L.    1½ miles SE of Sennen SW358237
S.    Two levels adjoin the cliff footpath and open out in the bay itself, probably unproductive trials for tin. Near Lower Bosistow Farm, SW365240, is the granite masonry of a water wheel stamps used by the old tinners, and another much shorter level which peters out after a few feet.

## WEST WHEAL MARGARET

D.    1860–1870
L.    Crows-an-Wra, 2¾ miles E of Sennen SW396272
M/O.  15 tons tin
S.    The portals of two levels can be found in dense undergrowth south of Crella Farm, and east of the stream. A single shaft, now obscured by brambles, is on the left of the track that leads to Boscarn.

## AVARACK AND NANCOTHAN

D.    circa 1850's
L.    2 miles SW of Penzance SW443289
M/O.  Small quantities of tin
S.    Shaft, now flooded, water-wheel pit and leat situated in a small

top north of Trevega Farm — a conspicuous object viewed for some distance across St. Ives Bay. Lower down the bracken-covered slope and adjacent to the North Cliffs footpath are the ivy-covered walls of the pumping engine house and stack. The shaft has been filled, and several adits can be seen at the base of the cliffs at low tide.

valley west of the Penzance-Lower Drift road. Another shaft, in undergrowth, is to be found at the head of the valley nearer the reservoir.

Dir.    Take the track to Nancothan from the Penzance road, then turn left into the woods bordering the stream that flows from the Drift Reservoir. The workings are half-way into the wood, on the north bank of the stream.

## BOSWARTHEN

D.    1852–1854
L.    ½ mile S of Sancreed SW415292
M/O.    10 tons tin
S.    Several shafts, two adits and some overgrown burrows can be found in the vicinity of Boswarthen Farm. The walls of a dry or possibly a small stamps engine house stand in a copse above the farm.

## ST. IVES WHEAL ALLEN

D.    1860–1868
L.    ¾ mile W of St. Ives SW498399
M/O.    116 tons tin
S.    The tall, solitary granite chimney stack of this mine stands near the track to Trevalgen, and is a conspicuous object west of the road from St. Ives to Zennor.

## ROSEWALL AND RANSOM UNITED

D.    1839–1876
L.    1¼ miles SW of St. Ives SW497393
M/O.    1,500 tons tin
S.    The remains of this small tin producer lie scattered over the bracken-covered slope of Rosewall Hill. Two engine houses survive, one reduced to the bob wall and the other an ivy-covered ruin. Two small stacks stand near the summit of the hill.

## TYRINGHAM CONSOLS (WEST PROVIDENCE)

D.    1861–1868
L.    1½ miles SW of St. Ives SW494386
M/O.    1,535 tons copper; 790 tons tin
S.    The site of this mine is identified today by one wall of an engine house standing in a field to the west of Higher Bussow Farm.

## GIEW (SOUTH PROVIDENCE)
D.      1838-1922
L.      $2\frac{1}{4}$ miles S of St. Ives SW501369
M/O.  145 tons of tin recorded
S.      A very prominent and well preserved pumping engine house standing beside the B3311 road near Trink Hill. The brick portion of the stack has been dismantled, and the original iron window frames are still intact in the window openings. A substantial part of the mine's boiler house also survives. The tall, graceful stack and other masonry in the valley below at Penderleath, SW497375, forms part of a dis-used china clay working where china clay was found in the area around Towednack.

Plate 2:  *Giew Mine*

## WHEAL SISTERS
D.      1825-1900
L.      $2\frac{1}{2}$ miles S of St. Ives SW508363
M/O.  12,950 tons tin; 10,700 tons copper
S.      The Wheal Sisters group of mines were amongst the most productive in the area. A large, ivy-covered pumping engine

house stands on waste ground at the junction of the road to Trencrom, between Trink and Trencrom Hills, SW513367. The Wheal Kitty part of the sett exhibits the remains of a smaller engine house in a more ruined condition. This is situated in a corner of a field north west of Polpeor at SW506362.

Plate 3: *Wheal Sisters*

# Mount's Bay — Coast and Inland

## TREGURTHA DOWNS

D.     1860–1902

L.     ½ mile W of Goldsithney SW539311

M/O.  1,295 tons tin

S.     A finely preserved 80″ pumping engine house, still roofed, and built in the same style as the larger house at East Wheal Rose, stands on the site with two attendant stacks. The beam engine that occupied this building is now 'in situ' on Robinson's Shaft at South Crofty.

## PROSPER UNITED (MARAZION MINES also TREVARTHIAN DOWNS)

D.    1830–1873

L.    1¼ miles W of Goldsithney SW535317

M/O.  22,500 tons copper; 830 tons tin; 1,165 tons arsenic

S.    A large ivy-covered engine house stands in a field to the south of Trevarthian Farm. Most of the dumps are now overgrown and the shafts filled.

## WHEAL SPEEDWELL

D.    1819–1854

L.    2½ miles E of Marazion SW558292

M/O.  11,360 tons copper

S.    The small, arched bob wall of this mine stands amidst extensive dumps by the side of the track leading from the A394 to Prussia Cove, on Rosudgeon Common.

Plate 4:  *Wheal Speedwell*

## WHEAL GREY

D.    1838–1910

L.    1 mile W of Breage SW595291

M/O.  116 tons tin

S.    The site at Wheal Grey was mined both for tin and china clay, and a small engine house and stack stands near Tresowes Green, near the road to Balwest. The china clay workings are obscured by undergrowth and trees, whilst three chimney stacks can be seen north of the A394 Helston road nearer Germoe.

## GREAT WESTERN

D.    1870–1886

L.    ½ mile N of Prah Sands SW581288

M/O.  412 tons tin; 50 tons arsenical pyrites

S.    Two tall chimney stacks overlook the profusion of holiday chalets that now cover the site of these old workings around Prah Sands. Most of the burrows and shafts have now been cleared and filled-in because of re-development in this area.

## WHEAL PROSPER

D.    1860–1866

L.    2 miles W of Porthleven SW590270

M/O.  7 tons tin

S.    Restored by the National Trust in 1971, the graceful 30″ pumping engine house of this small tin producer stands on the verge of Rinsey Cliff adjacent to the coastal footpath.

## TREWAVAS HEAD MINE

D.    1835–1846

L.    1½ miles W of Porthleven SW600266

M/O.  17,500 tons copper

S.    Two granite engine houses, one with a separate stack, are perched on the precipitous cliffs near Porthleven in almost as spectacular a setting as the more familiar buildings at Botallack. The stump of a second stack is situated near the old miner's trackway that spirals down the face of Trewavas Head Cliff.

## WHEAL PENROSE and WHEAL ROSE

D.    1840–1872

L.    ¼ mile SE of Porthleven SW634252

M/O. Only 175 tons of lead recorded

S. There are extensive dumps and waste tips alongside the footpath to Loe Bar, where good mineral specimens can still be found. Old levels and shafts in the low cliffs have caused severe subsidence over the past few years. The main adit of Wheal Rose has its portal adjacent to Loe Bar at SW645243.

## TREGEMBO

D. 1883–1888

L. East of Relubbas SW571318

M/O. 112 tons tin; 6 tons copper

S. A small pumping engine house and two stacks are to be found south of the B3280 road near Tregembo Farm, overlooking the River Hayle.

## TINDENE

D. 1887–1892

L. $\frac{1}{2}$ mile SE of Relubbas SW575314

M/O. 169 tons tin

S. The well preserved 65″ pumping engine house stands in swampy ground adjoining the River Hayle, north west of Trescowe.

## WEST GODOLPHIN

D. 1860–1890

L. $1\frac{3}{4}$ miles E of St. Hilary SW585313

M/O. 1,520 tons tin; 214 tons copper

S. The large pumping engine house of this mine, known locally as Wheal Junket, stands on the slope of Godolphin Hill above the road to Trescowe. Below the road, at SW580319, are two small stacks marking the site of the stamps, near the track leading to the River Hayle.

## GREAT WORK

D. 1810–1885

L. 2 miles NW of Breage SW596308

M/O. 6,256 tons tin; 1,020 tons copper

S. The 60″ pumping engine house and separate stepped stack standing on the site is situated between Godolphin and Tregoning Hills — a very conspicuous object viewed great distances from the west.

## WHEAL METAL (NEW WHEAL VOR)

D.  1858–1901
L.  1 mile NE of Breage SW629298
M/O.  3,700 tons tin
S.  A massively constructed 85″ pumping engine house stands on private ground near a small wood riddled with old men's workings, to the east of Carleen Village.

## WHEAL METAL AND FLOW

D.  1885–1901
L.  ¾ mile NE of Breage SW622295
M/O.  540 tons of tin
S.  There is a small stamps engine house and stack, with several shafts and overgrown dumps, on Carnmeal Downs. Also to be found are traces of the dressing floors including some buddles, although undergrowth is gradually obscuring the site.

## POLLADRAS DOWN

D.  Included with the working of Wheal Vor
L.  ½ mile N of Carleen SW614311
M/O.  Included with that of Wheal Vor
S.  An ivy-covered ruined engine house stands on the sett of one of several mines in the area included in the Great Wheal Vor United Group, a short distance south east of Godolphin Cross.

# Helston — Wendron

## GREAT WHEAL LOVELL

D.  1871–1876
L.  2½ miles NE of Helston SW693305
M/O.  64 tons tin
S.  Due to road expansion of the A394 in 1986, the ivy-covered bob wall of this small tin mine was demolished, and only two stacks remain on the site near Manhay. The stamps engine house, also shrouded in ivy, still survives in a corner of a field to the west of the road, but this is in a poor state of preservation.

## SOUTH LOVELL

D.  1860–1882
L.  1¾ miles NW of Constantine SW705301
M/O.  21 tons tin

15

S.    The ruined chimney stack and the crumbling remains of a dry stand in a wooded valley near the stream slightly west of Ninnis Farm.

## BEACON HILL

D.    circa 1870's
L.    3 miles NE of Helston SW692308
M/O.  No records — tin
S.    A small, granite chimney stack is situated on waste ground near the summit of the hill of the same name, erected in the 1870's.

## EAST WHEAL LOVELL

D.    1859–1891
L.    1½ miles E of Wendron SW699314
M/O.  2,405 tons tin
S.    Familiar to travellers on the Helston-Falmouth road is the engine house of another of the many mines in the area to have worked under the name of 'Lovell'. This stands on a ridge to the west of the road near the hamlet of Carnebone.

Plate 5: *East Wheal Lovell*

16

## RETANNA HILL — *25*
D. 1835–1868
L. 2¾ miles NE of Wendron SW716328
M/O. 22 tons tin
S. A single chimney stack, brick portion missing, stands in a field by the side of the A394 road near Butteriss Gate.

## MEDLYN MOOR — *24*
D. 1874–1880
L. 1¼ miles E of Porkellis SW707337
M/O. 80 tons tin
S. The well preserved 40″ pumping engine house stands in a marshy valley intersected by the dried-up beds of ancient tin streams worked by the old men. *SEE NO. 16 EDS*

## BASSET AND GRYLLS — *12 692–33I WRWDW DIN*
D. 1852–1914
L. Short distance S of Porkellis SW694328
M/O. 4,650 tons tin
S. Tyack's 60″ pumping engine house is in good condition and stands at the entrance to a small wood bordering the Porkellis–Wendron road. A single stack and a few concrete foundations of the dressing floors at SW688327 marks the site of the more recent re-workings.

## WHEAL ENYS — *11*
D. 1853–1859
L. ¼ mile NW of Porkellis SW691336
M/O. 259 tons tin
S. The stamps engine house stands on the slope of Porkellis Moor Extra openings for windows and the built-up bob wall indicate that at some period the building was used as a dwelling.

## CALVADNACK — *21*
D. 1850–1875
L. 1 mile NE of Porkellis SW699348
M/O. 1,328 tons tin
S. The crumbling remains of the engine house, now reduced to the lower walls, stand near the track crossing White Alice Moor. Several un-fenced shafts and overgrown burrows abound in the area.

## WHEAL ANN (TRUMPET CONSOLS)
D.     1854–1880
L.     ½ mile SW of Wendron SW678304
M/O.  4,510 tons tin; 20 tons copper
S.     A large pumping engine house and separate stack can be seen in a field west of Crahan Farm, on the Wheal Ann sett. Wheal Dream's site is identifiable today by the smaller whim engine house and boiler house standing beside the B3297 road slightly west of Wheal Ann, at SW673302.

## WEST WENDRON CONSOLS
D.     1862–1867
L.     ½ mile N of Wendron SW681316
M/O.  No recorded output — tin
S.     The base walls of a small engine house and stack, now partly reduced to rubble, can be found at the edge of a field a short distance north of Trenear.

## WHEAL FURSEDEN
D.     1860–1861
L.     ¾ mile NW of Wendron SW669317
M/O.  Obscure, unproductive trial for tin — no records
S.     Very ruinous, smally constructed engine house, covered in undergrowth, on the valley slope above the stream flowing into the River Cober. Shaft is filled in.
Dir.    Just over a mile north of Wendron, turn left at the crossroads at SW678330. Proceed down the road for ½ mile, take the left fork past Bodilly Veor and then turn right onto the footpath that crosses the stream near the old mill. The stream is passable at this point — go up the right hand fork that climbs the valley side. The engine house is in a clump of trees adjacent to the path that skirts the top of the valley to Bosoar.

## SOUTH WHEAL TREASURE
D.     circa 1830–1840
L.     3 miles E of Mullion, on Goonhilly Downs SW718197
M/O.  No records — copper
S.     The ruined walls of three buildings, comprising an engine house of small construction, a larger miner's dwelling or counthouse and an old dry, stand at the head of 'Mine Valley' on the

Downs, south of the satellite station. An opencut, some 200 ft. in length with an average depth of 8 ft. and partly filled with water, runs through the sett, terminating in a flooded level. Overgrown dumps are scattered over the moors in the vicinity of these workings.

Dir. This virtually forgotten mine is in a very isolated position and quite hard to find. The easiest route is to proceed north up the moorland road from Kuggar (SW724163) until a coniferous plantation appears on the left of the road near Croft Pascoe Pool. Go down the track that divides this wood into two halves — this leads to a fence that surrounds the plantation. Over the fence, and descend the shallow valley, walking due north towards the satellite 'dishes'. There is a boggy patch of ground where the valley is intersected by a stream, but this is negotiable. A long clamber upwards on the opposite slope brings you to the mine and its remains.

# NANCEGOLLAN

D. 1853–1870
L. East of Nancegollan Village SW640324
M/O. 6 tons tin
S. The graceful engine house and stack of this unproductive tin mine stands in a field near the abandoned railway line and north of the road to Porkellis.

Plate 6: *Nancegollan*

19

## POLCREBO DOWNS (CARBONA)

D.     1860–1890
L.     ¾ mile NE of Nancegollan SW647331
M/O.   102 tons tin
S.     The small stump of a chimney stack and extensive waste tips litter the bleak moorland overlooking the village. The bob wall of the engine house, once a conspicuous object viewed from Nancegollan, has now been reduced to a pile of rubble from the effects of the weather.

# Around Camborne

## ROSEWORTHY

L.     2¼ miles W of Camborne SW604411
S.     The tall chimney stack of Roseworthy arsenic works, nearly 100ft. in height, stands above Nancemellin on the valley side. This was erected in the early part of this century to deal with the production of arsenic from surrounding workings.

## SOUTH ALFRED (BANDOWERS MINE)

D.     1819–1866
L.     2 miles SE of Hayle SW588362
M/O.   3 tons copper
S.     One ivy-covered and very ruinous wall of the pumping engine house still survives from this small copper working, situated in a corner of a boggy, ochrous field west of Tregotha Farm.

## TREVOOLE

D.     1827–1862
L.     1 mile N of Praze-an-Beeble SW638371
M/O.   3,411 tons copper
S.     A large, well preserved pumping engine house, and a separate stack of the now demolished whim, can be seen on waste ground beside the B3303 road at Trevoole Moor.

## SOUTH CONDURROW

D.     1848–1920
L.     1 mile SE of Camborne SW660385
M/0.   11,430 tons tin; 1,060 tons copper
S.     Marshall's 60″ pumping engine house and 26″ whim form a fine pair on Newton Moor on the outskirts of Troon Village.

## GRENVILLE UNITED

D.     1900–1920

L.     $1\frac{1}{4}$ miles SE of Camborne SW664387

M/O.  14,620 tons tin; 2,330 tons copper; some arsenic

S.     The stamps and pumping engine houses on the King Edward part of the sett stand in the grounds of the Camborne School of Mines. Goold's 80″ pumping engine house, once a massive structure beside the road from Newton to Carnkie, was wantonly demolished in 1984 and only a fractional part of this building now remains.

## WHEAL GRENVILLE

D.     1820–1920

L.     $1\frac{1}{2}$ miles SE of Camborne SW668388

M/O.  Included with Grenville United

S.     A huge 90″ pumping engine house stands on Fortescue's Shaft, with the nearby 40″ whim house, both in good condition. On a ridge to the south of the road is the stamps engine house and dressing floors marking the site of New Stamps.

## EAST GRENVILLE

D.     1820–1875

L.     $1\frac{3}{4}$ miles SE of Camborne SW674391

M/O.  327 tons copper; 23 tons tin

S.     Although situated near the larger Grenville United Group, this mine was never as productive as its wealthy neighbours. Two small engine houses still survive on Bolenowe Moor, both in fair condition.

## GREAT CONDURROW

D.     1860–1913

L.     $\frac{3}{4}$ mile SE of Camborne SW661393

M/O.  30,495 tons copper; 2,030 tons tin

S.     The 80″ pumping engine house on Neame's Shaft is another large mining relic in the Camborne area in a fine state of preservation, and a very prominent object viewed from the west of the town.

## BREA STAMPS

L.     1 mile E of Camborne SW666398

A single brick chimney stack and the remains of long abandoned dressing floors, with a few wooden launders in dilapidated condition, can be found in ever-encroaching undergrowth on either side of the stream flowing from Bolenowe Moor through Brea Village. There are also the ruins of an old dry beside the road leading into the village at SW667404.

## DOLCOATH

D.    1799–1920

L.    $\frac{1}{2}$ mile NE of Camborne SW661404

M/O.  350,000 tons copper; 80,000 tons tin

S.    Considering that this was once Cornwall's premier tin mine, very little remains at surface today to give any indication of how large an area the mine covered in its' heyday. At SW661404 is the engine house, boiler house and stack on new Sump Shaft. At SW652397, to the right of the lane leading to Pengegon and adjacent to the Penzance railway line, is the 65″ pumping engine house on Stray Park Shaft. In a direct line east, at SW658401, is the house of the other 65″ engine to have worked for the mine, on Harriet's Shaft, shorn of the upper brick portion of the

Plate 8: *Dolcoath — New Sump Shaft*

stack. William's Shaft, 3,000 ft. deep and brick-lined, is on the slope of Carn Entral at SW661400. The walls of the traversing winding house surround this shaft, the deepest to be sunk in the country; the shaft itself has been capped for safety reasons. Most of Dolcoath's once extensive dumps and tailings have now been levelled due to the growth of Camborne itself.

## COOK'S KITCHEN
D.     1815–1905
L.     ½ mile SE of Tuckingmill SW664406
M/O.  40,920 tons copper; 8,859 tons tin; 120 tons arsenic
S.     The pumping and whim engine houses of this once famous mine, together with the ruins of the boiler house, form a conspicuous pair beside the railway line, on the borders of South Crofty.

## SOUTH TINCROFT
D.     1815–1921 (with TINCROFT)
L.     ¾ mile SE of Tuckingmill SW668407
M/O.  With TINCROFT — 112,700 tons copper; 32,972 tons tin; 6,530 tons arsenic

Plate 7: *South Tincroft*

23

S.    A large stamps engine house stands sentinal beside the road to Brea Village. Nearby are the arched remains of the horizontal winding house, in good condition, and a single chimney stack. Of Tincroft Mine itself, and the vast burrows and tailings that remained up until the end of the 1960's, virtually nothing of these workings are now visible, the whole area levelled and buried under re-development and the leisure centre.

## CARN BREA

D.    1833–1920
L.    1 mile E of Pool SW676409
M/O.  237,493 tons copper; 29,600 tons tin; 4,140 tons arsenic
S.    Part of a stamps engine house dating from the 1850's remains, with an attendant, blackened and stepped chimney stack. Several shafts and a line of old burrows can be traced along the lower slopes of Carn Brea almost to Blowinghouse.

Plate 10: *Carn Brea*

24

# SOUTH CROFTY

D.    1854–present
L.    Pool, near Camborne SW668414
M/O.  To 1920 – 36,908 tons copper; 12,051 tons tin; 3,250 tons arsenic; 1,379 tons wolfram
S.    Robinson's 80″ beam engine remains 'in situ' on the site, preserved by the National Trust. The 90″ pumping engine house constructed entirely of concrete, formerly on New Cook's Shaft, has now been demolished.

Plate 9:   *Stamps engine house — Tolvaddon Downs*

# TOLVADDON DOWNS — TUCKINGMILL VALLEY

L.    ¾ mile W of Pool SW659415
S.    The Tuckingmill Valley that runs through Tolvaddon Downs, situated behind Cornwall Technical College, still carries the mineral enriched streams that eventually flow out to the sea at Gwithian as the 'Red River'. In the past, numerous mines, notably the Seton group, worked copper lodes on the valley sides, and the streams themselves were exploited for their mineral content. East Pool Mine also utilised part of the valley for the treatment of both tin and arsenic from the early 1900's.

Up until 1970, the valley formed a unique industrial museum of sorts, with several of the old tin dressing plants still in operation. However, due to the Scorrier–Camborne road expansion programme in 1973, the decision was made to 'clean the valley up'. Wheal Seton's fine 70″ pumping engine house, which dominated the west flank of the valley, was wantonly demolished, despite a huge local outcry. Also gone are the two 80 ft. high blackened arsenic stacks that towered above the minor road to Illogan, together with their extensive flues and condensing chambers. The tin works and dressing floors have been dismantled, shafts filled, burrows levelled and stacks toppled. What remains, now that the by-pass bisects the valley; three solitary chimneys, a small stamps engine house dating from the East Pool period of operation at SW656419, some old settling tanks and a few grassed-over dumps. The chance for an industrial showpiece, such as the site at Tolgus Tin, has been lost forever.

## EAST POOL

D.      1835–1930
L.      Pool, near Camborne SW673415
M/O.    88,300 tons copper; 38,490 tons tin; 31,722 tons arsenic; 2,820 tons wolfram
S.      Mitchell's 30″ winding house, engine 'in situ', stands by the A30 road, preserved by the National Trust and now worked for the public by compressed air.

## EAST POOL AND AGAR

D.      1840–1949
L.      Pool SW676418
M/O.    3,033 tons copper (as Wheal Agar)
S.      The 90″ pumping engine house on Taylor's Shaft, with separate stack and engine 'in situ' has also been preserved by the Trust. The shaft is still utilised for ventilation purposes by South Crofty.

# Around Redruth

## WEST TOLGUS
D.     1832–1883
L.     1 mile W of Redruth SW681420
M/O.  47,700 tons copper
S.     The small stamps engine house that formerly stood overlooking the Tolgus Valley that runs to Vogue Beloth was demolished in 1973 — the stump of a stack remains, with some grassed-over burrows.

## WHEAL TEHIDY
D.     1834–1865
L.     1 mile W of Redruth SW684419
M/O.  2,657 tons copper
S.     A small, ivy-covered chimney stack with a square stone base is at the head of the valley adjacent to West Tolgus. A ruined building in undergrowth a short distance west could possibly be an old miner's dry or dwelling.

## TOLGUS
L.     $1\frac{1}{4}$ miles W of Redruth SW681426
S.     Three blackened chimney stacks and the remains of some condensing chambers are grouped at the bottom of West Tolgus lane, near the by-pass flyover. Another stack and a colossal dump of burnt tailings are to be found further down the valley at SW682427. The ruins of a dry stand next to the lane that leads to Mount Tolgus, and yet another arsenic stack with some crumbling flues is at SW689430, above the Old Portreath road. Tolgus Tin Works, $1\frac{1}{2}$ miles from Redruth on the B3300 at SW689443, is at present engaged in the treatment of tin from surrounding streams and the working from the Tolgus group.

## GREAT NORTH TOLGUS
D.     1832–1862
L.     $1\frac{1}{2}$ miles NW of Redruth SW688431–SW687448
M/O.  4,120 tons copper
S.     The dumps and shafts of this mine are scattered over the valley sides from Gilberts Coombe to the junction of the Portreath–Porthtowan road. The stump of a chimney stack can

be seen on a bank beside the road near this junction. Opposite the road, a striking line of five air shafts crossing a field can be located north of the Tolgus stream works.

## WEST PEEVOR (TRELEIGH CONSOLS)

D.   1879–1889
L.   1¼ miles N of Redruth SW705441
M/O. 1,200 tons tin; 20 tons arsenic
S.   A picturesque, ivy-covered stamps engine house with a nearby smaller pumping engine house are situated in the valley below the main workings of Wheal Peevor. The latter building has been reduced in size to the height of the bob wall as a result of an unsuccessful re-opening of the mine in the 1960's.

## WHEAL PEEVOR

D.   1872–1912
L.   1¼ miles N of Redruth SW708442
M/O. 3,280 tons tin
S.   A striking and familiar group of engine houses viewed from the Scorrier by-pass, comprising the 70″ pumping, 32″ stamps and whim engine houses. A truncated stack and piles of 'deads' litter the valley slope to West Peevor, and another stack is on waste ground to the east on North Downs.

## PENNANCE

D.   1866–1872
L.   1 mile SE of Redruth SW712405
M/O. 590 tons copper
S.   A very prominent, well preserved pumping engine house standing beside a large dump on the slope of Carn Marth above Lanner — the mine itself was a poor producer of copper.

## PEDNANDREA

D.   1854—1891
L.   Redruth SW704420
M/O. 7,700 tons tin; 1,090 tons copper
S.   The well known stepped stack of this mine, constructed of killas, overlooks the town, although much reduced from its former height of 140 ft. because of the close proximity of the railway.

Plate 12: *Pennance*

## WHEAL UNY

D.     1800–1893
L.     $\frac{3}{4}$ mile S of Redruth SW695408
M/O.   2,825 tons copper; 7,660 tons tin
S.     The 70″ pumping engine house and whim on Hind's Shaft form a conspicuous pair on high ground south of the town. Most of the dumps have been levelled, although a small stack stands lower down the valley side, probably used for ore dressing.

## BASSET MINES

D.     1815–1919
L.     $1\frac{1}{2}$ miles S of Redruth, at Carnkie SW687399
M/O.   290,118 tons copper; 43,134 tons tin
S.     The substantial remains of this once rich group of mines still dominate the landscape in the vicinity of Carnkie, despite land reclamation in recent years. Some of the most impressive relics left from large scale mining in West Cornwall can today be seen at the following sites:
*SW689402* — Large stamps engine house, boiler house, and

29

Plate 11:  *Lyle's pumping engine house — Basset Mines*

three stacks on the West Basset Stamps part of the sett.

*SW690401* - Lyle's 80″ pumping engine house and nearby whim, with boiler house and stack, all in good condition.

*SW690398* — A small stamps engine house that contained two beam engines, hence a double bob wall, three stacks, ruins of dressing floors and extensive waste tips all scarring the hillside to the south of the village, marking the site of **Basset Old Stamps**.

*SW698401* — The arched remains of a bob wall and concrete buildings dating from the last period of production.

*SW682397* — A large bob wall constructed of dressed granite blocks and dated 1854 stands beside the road to Piece.

30

*SW680395* — This is the site of the Wheal Frances sett of the Basset Group. The most conspicuous building is Marriott's 40″/80″ engine house whose massive walls enclose the brick-lined circular shaft, 500 fathoms deep. The boiler house and other associated buildings cluster around this shaft, but most of the once extensive line of dumps have been levelled and landscaped.

*SW676395* — At this site are Pascoe's pumping and whim engine houses, with boiler house, all in a good state of preservation.

## TRESAVEAN

D.    1815–1927

L.    ½ mile SE of Lanner SW719395

M/O.  167,720 tons copper; 1,678 tons tin

S.    The dumps, burrows and shafts of this once rich copper producer still cover the slopes of Lanner Moor. One engine house survives, brick top of stack missing, the only substantial building remaining on the site.

## NORTH WHEAL VIRGIN

D.    1807–1820

L.    ½ mile S of Portreath SW663447

M/O.  No records — unproductive prospecting and trials carried out in the Portreath Moor area.

S.    There is an old lichen-covered buddle in Feadon (Illogan) Woods on the bank of the stream. On the east bank of the stream is a caved-in shaft or adit issuing a stream of ochrous water. Several ancient quarries and walls can be found in these woods.

## WEST UNITED HILLS

D.    1844–1854

L.    2¼ miles NE of Portreath SW691460

M/O.  No records — an amalgamation of several small prospects that worked copper lodes on Nancekuke Common.

S.    Although virtually unknown, traces of this mine, which appeared to have covered a considerable area, still exist in the vicinity of Cambrose. There are some overgrown burrows and shaft dumps on either side of the road leading to the dis-used Nancekuke school and School Farm. In a corner of a field to the south east of the school are the ruined walls of an old dry. Immediately east are gorse-covered dumps and two air shafts on the course of a N–E lode. A fenced, flooded shaft of small dimensions is situated in the valley adjacent to a stream at SW688463, and there are some more scattered tips and grassed-over burrows near Southview Farm at SW686457.

# The North Cliffs — Chapel Porth to Hayle

The North Cliffs is the name given to the tract of rugged highlands, rising to over 300 ft., north of Camborne and Redruth. Although lying outside the highly mineralised zones of these towns, The North Cliffs have been prospected and mined over a long period, and evidence left from past mining activity can still be found.

On the cliff top at Mulgram Hill, slightly south of Chapel Porth, is the bob wall, shafts and extensive dumps of WHEAL CHARLOTTE (SW698492). Active from 1834–1840, the mine produced 2,800 tons of copper and the old miner's trackway still connects the workings to the cove below, where there are the portals of two adits. Between this mine

Plate 13:  *Bob wall — Wheal Charlotte*

32

and Porthtowan, several levels can be seen in the face of the cliffs at low water. Most of these are of an exploratory nature, terminating in dead ends after 200-300 ft. and water-logged.

Across from Porthtowan Beach are the high commonlands of Nancekuke, intensively prospected in the past by a veritable host of small mines, including WHEAL VINCENT, METAL WORK, WHEAL WEST, WHEAL CLARENCE, CLIFF DOWN and STERRAN AND TYE. WHEAL LUSHINGTON, whose engine house dating from the 1870's stands on Porthtowan Beach (SW693478), and has now been converted into a cafe, was at one time included in this group, and the whole network was last worked in the 1920's–1930's at the Sally Bottoms site near Kerriack Cove. A square concrete stack and flue dating from this latter period of activity still adorns the cliff top (SW681473).

Plate 14: *Sally Bottoms*

Because of the intermingling of boundaries, the individual mines are difficult to identify today. The adit portal of Wheal Vincent is at the base of the cliff at SW689478 and is blocked by debris about 60 ft. from the entrance. The other levels and adits in the next bay are now inaccessible due to the fact that Tobban Horse Rock collapsed against the main cliff several years ago, thus effectively sealing them off. Sally Bottoms main drainage adit can be reached at low tide by a tortuous pathway down the

33

cliff face — there are various openings in the cliff here, some revealing old ladders and tramways. Sally Bottoms main engine shaft, sunk 250 ft., intersected the old men's levels and has now been capped with concrete. From 1823 to 1881, the group produced 2,610 tons copper, 558 tons tin, 747 tons lead, 200 tons pyrites, 13,700 oz silver and 1 ton zinc. Many of the dozen or so shafts have recently been capped, but there are some more extensive workings along the small valley from Factory Farm to the cliffs at SW678469, including the ruined walls of a small dressing plant and three buddles, with several more levels in the surrounding cliff faces.

On Portreath Beach can be seen the old men's levels of a small copper mine entitled WHEAL MARY (SW652453). The adit portal is midway up the cliff at Battery Point, and stoping is very much in evidence in an adjacent sea cave. The passage leads to another entrance behind the hotel on the cliff top, which has been sealed by the owners. From 1853–1857, this mine produced 28 tons copper.

From Portreath, the ground rises steeply to Reskajeage Downs. One mile west is Basset's Cove, which was extensively worked in the 1840's by a venture known as the NORTH CLIFFS MINING COMPANY. It was possible to gain access to several adits and levels here by circumnavigating a crumbling cliff path which lead into the cove, but subsidences over the past few years have rendered these old mine workings inaccessible (SW637443).

Further along the cliffs, at the inlet next to Hell's Mouth (SW600429) are another set of levels at the base of the cliffs, all unsuccessful trials for tin and copper. A similar length of passageway in the adjacent Fishing Cove also peters out after about 50 ft.

At Gwithian, across from the Red River estuary, the downs level out to a low line of crumbling cliffs that continue to Hayle Towans. These cliffs and the sand dune area behind them exhibit scant traces of a few long forgotten ventures that have worked here. The first such mine was WHEAL EMILY, an insignificant sett that produced a few tons of copper in the 1860's. The adit opens out onto the cliffs at Strap Point (SW579415), but has been bricked up to keep people out. Another level can be found in the nearby sand dunes. BOILING WELL MINE (SW577397) worked on Upton Towans from 1821–1861, producing copper, lead and zinc. No buildings remain from this mine, although numerous overgrown burrows and filled-in shafts abound in the area. Of the two other mines to have been in production on both Upton and Phillack Towans, WHEAL CUPOLA (SW568387) and LOGGANS

MINE (SW574391), nothing much remains except for undulations, scattered grassed-over dumps and two or three shafts.

On Hayle Towans, the track leading to the beach passes one of the adits of WHEAL LUCY. The main adit of this mine was formerly to be found at the western end of Black Cliff, SW555388, and this gave access to over $\frac{1}{2}$ mile of shallow workings. Cliff falls have since obliterated the entrance to this interesting mine, although another much smaller level is nearer Phillack Towans on the low cliff line. From 1872–1895, Wheal Lucy produced 24 tons of tin. All of the shafts have long been capped and can be seen as grassed-filled depressions in the surrounding dunes.

# Porthtowan — Scorrier

## TYWARNHAYLE
D.  1826–1906
L.  $\frac{3}{4}$ mile SE of Porthtowan SW699472
M/O.  115,388 tons copper; some lead, tin and pyrites
S.  The widespread workings of this copper mine cover both sides of the canyon-like valley leading to Porthtowan. At SW700472, perched on the valley top, is the 70" pumping engine house of United Hills, whose underground levels honeycombing the hillside are used for training and surveying purposes. Below United Hill's mountainous dumps (two stacks also survive) is another large engine house with a castellated stack at SW703468, marking the site of Wheal Ellen, also entitled Old Wheal Basset. A very ancient ivy-covered engine house and stack at SW698472 is on the site of the original Tywarnhayle workings, with another tall stack a short distance west down the road.

## WHEAL MUSIC
D.  1815–1825
L.  1 mile SE of Porthtowan SW704470
M/O.  4,600 tons copper
S.  A vast openwork in the form of a gigantic circular pit, an acre in area and over 100 ft. deep, can be seen across the road north of Wheal Ellen's engine house, where the ore was quarried rather than mined.

# WHEAL TOWAN
D.  1800–1835
L.  $\frac{1}{4}$ mile E of Porthtowan SW696480
M/O.  26,058 tons copper
S.  The quite considerable burrows, dumps and shafts of Wheal Towan still scar the valley sides beside the road that climbs out of Porthtowan to St. Agnes.

# WHEAL ROSE
D.  1826–1872
L.  $\frac{1}{4}$ mile NW of Scorrier SW718449
M/O.  12,820 tons copper; 18 tons tin
S.  A small, well preserved engine house that worked for one of the numerous mines included in the North Downs Group stands beside the Scorrier–Porthtowan road a short distance west of Wheal Rose Farm.

# NORTH TRESKERBY
D.  1859–1892
L.  $\frac{1}{2}$ mile N of Scorrier SW724451
M/O.  19,270 tons copper; 150 tons tin
S.  A prominent, three-storied 80″ pumping engine house standing on Doctor's Shaft is a conspicuous object on a ridge to the west of the A30 road. This fine building is in a good state of preservation.

# HALLENBEAGLE
D  1845–1846
L.  North east of Scorrier SW726446
M/O.  30,580 tons copper
S.  The 70″ pumping engine house of this mine is a familiar sight to railway travellers entering Redruth, as the workings cover both sides of the rail track. Near this relic stand the stack and ruined walls of the whim.

# TRESKERBY (WHEAL CHANCE)
D.  1815–1822, re-worked 1922–1927
L.  $\frac{1}{4}$ mile S of Scorrier SW723438
M/O.  51,000 tons copper
S.  A line of impressively large calciners and flues lead up to a tall

chimney whose top can be seen above the tree line in the woods west of Scorrier house. This dates from the latter period of production, as do the extensive waste tips surrounding the stack.

# St. Day — Chacewater

## WHEAL GRAMBLA (ST. AUBYN AND GRAMBLA)

D.     1843–1893
L.     1 mile W of St. Day SW716422
M/O.  12,510 tons copper; 97 tons tin
S.     A finely proportioned pumping engine house wreathed in ivy still stands beside the slip road between South Trefula and Ninnis, together with several shafts and overgrown dumps.

Plate 17: *Wheal Grambla*

## PARK–AN–CHY (EAST TRESKERBY)

D.  circa 1860's, re-worked 1910–1930
L.  ¾ mile NW of St. Day SW721432
M/O.  Small quantities of tin and wolfram
S.  A huge slatey dump and single chimney stack remain a conspicuous feature on the slope of Pink Moor. The stump of a second stack and some concrete out-buildings are also on the site, together with a caved-in gunnis, now fenced for safety.


## POLDICE

D.  1815–1919
L.  ¾ mile E of St. Day SW743428
M/O.  108,698 tons copper; 1,525 tons tin; 825 tons arsenic; 321 tons ochre
S.  One chimney stack stands amidst vast tonnages of spoil tips, numerous shafts (some extremely deep and cavernous) and crumbling walls. Some landscaping of the dumps has taken place here over the past few years, but the remains of the arsenic treatment buildings, including calciners and flues, are still on the site. An old ivy-covered miner's dry is on the valley side in undergrowth at SW747429.


## UNITED MINES

D.  1815–1870, re-working of the dumps from 1900–1909
L.  1¼ miles E of St. Day SW746421
M/O.  Group — 934,795 tons copper; also quantities of tin, zinc and arsenic
S.  Up until the early 1970's, United Downs represented the bleakest, most barren area of derelict mining ground in Cornwall outside of the Caradon Hill district — a wilderness of dumps, burrows, countless shafts and numerous ruined buildings scarring the landscape from Twelveheads to Caharrack. Much of this has now vanished, partly by land reclamation, or by various companies re-working the considerable dumps. Due to the number of deep shafts still open on this once rich mining field, it was considered a few years ago dangerous and risky to set foot anywhere near the Downs, let alone across them. To a certain extent, this still applies, although many of the more cavernous shafts have now been capped or fenced, and the burrows levelled out. A few remaining

Plate 18: *Engine house — United Mines*

structures can still be found at the following locations:

*SW748414* — A large stamps engine house standing on a ridge and dating from the latter period of working. Eldon's 30″ pumping engine house, recently restored, and the walls of another larger engine house are also situated on this part of the sett.

*SW746421 to SW750424* — Between these two O/S references are the ruins of two more engine houses, two stacks and a well preserved blowing house. A great deal of work and excavation has been carried out in the deep valley separating United Downs and Goon Gumpas by Mount Wellington Mine and Wheal Jane in recent years.

*SW756420* — At this part of the sett, entitled Wheal Clifford, is an ivy-covered engine house, stack and boiler house, at the top of the valley near Cusvey.

Traces can also be found along the valley to Hale Mills of the Redruth and Chacewater Railway which served these mines from 1824 to their closure. A series of granite sleeper blocks, many now buried, skirt the valley sides from Twelveheads almost to Caharrack. A deep cutting crossed by a now overgrown bridge is near Hale Mills, and the tunnel through the cutting can still be entered at SW752424.

## WHEAL HENRY
D.      1815–1847
L.      1¼ miles E of St. Day SW752427
M/O.  1,860 tons copper
S.      One ivy-covered wall of the engine house stands on the valley side opposite to Goon Gumpas and the United Mines Group. Below this ruin is a particularly awsome collapsed gunnis branching out into a series of deep levels.

## UNITY WOOD (TOLGULLOW UNITED)
D.      1815–1873
L.      1 mile NE of St. Day SW736436
M/O.  22,792 tons copper; 1,220 tons tin
S.      The well preserved 70″ pumping and 26″ whim engine houses of this mine stand near Wheal Bush Farm, overlooking Unity Wood itself.

Plate 16:  *Unity Wood*

# WHEAL PROSPER

D.    1862–1870
L.    ¾ mile SE of Chacewater SW755432
M/O.  311 tons copper; 209 tons arsenic; 86 tons tin
S.    A small, unproductive copper producer whose sett today is marked by one ruined wall of an engine house and some grassed-over burrows on the banks of the stream that flows into the Carnon River.

# NANGILES

D.    1845–1906
L.    2¼ miles E of St. Day SW767422
M/O.  3,020 tons copper; 193 tons tin; quantities of zinc, pyrites, iron, arsenic and ochre
S.    The main engine shaft exhibits the remains of a bob wall, the remainder of the 80″ pumping engine house having been demolished in 1967, the date of the last re-working. Another very ruinous engine house stands nearby in dense undergrowth, overshadowed by mountainous waste tips. Lower down in the Carnon Valley, at Point Mills, is the site of the old Cornwall Arsenic Company, identifiable today by a tall, square calciner stack and the remains of some furnaces.

# KILLIFRETH

D    1859–1920
L.    1 mile SW of Chacewater SW734443
M/O.  4,060 tons tin; 681 tons copper; 360 tons arsenic
S.    Viewed from the hill descending Chacewater, the three engine houses of this mine (32″ stamps, 50″ and 85″ pumping) form an impressive silhouette on the skyline. The ruins of the whim, largely destroyed in an army demolition exercise, stands near Hawke's Shaft, whose large engine house has a distinctive tall stack. A single stack and some concrete masonry can be seen near the crossroads to Wheal Busy. To the south of Killifreth, old gunnises, levels and air shafts can be traced in Unity Wood, SW733437, marking the courses of lodes worked by both Killifreth and Unity Wood Mines. A wooden headframe was standing on one of these shafts in 1973 but has since been dismantled.

Plate 15: *Stamps engine house — Killifreth*

## WHEAL BUSY

L.      1 mile SW of Chacewater SW732444

S.      The gaunt ruins of the bob wall still survive on Black Dog Shaft beside the A390 to Chacewater. This was erected in the 1870's for a pumping engine that was never installed, due to an unsuccessful re-working.

## GREAT WHEAL BUSY

D.     1815–1923

L.     $\frac{3}{4}$ mile W of Chacewater SW740448

M/O.  104,700 tons copper; 1,758 tons tin; 26,650 tons mispickel; 735 tons arsenic

42

S.      Harvey's well preserved 85″ pumping engine house, stack and boiler house stand in a compact group near the remains of the smithy and stores, east of the road leading into the village. Between these buildings and the A390 are very extensive dumps, an imposing chimney stack and the remains of some calciners used for the production of arsenic.

# St. Agnes — Perranporth — Newquay

## CHARLOTTE UNITED (NORTH TOWAN)

D.      1820–1873
L.      1¼ miles NE of Porthtowan SW703488
M/O.  23,100 tons copper
S.      A small pumping engine house in a state of disrepair stands on the dump-strewn valley side above the Chapel Coombe stream. Portal of the adit, now flooded, is below this relic, adjoining the footpath to Chapel Porth.

Plate 19:   *Charlotte United*

43

# WHEAL FREEDOM and EAST CHARLOTTE

D.  1828–1862

L.  ½ mile S of Goonvrea SW704492

M/O.  90 tons copper; 13 tons tin

S.  There are some extensive dumps and the ruins of a dry or cottage in the small valley connecting Goonvrea with the Chapel Coombe Valley. At SW707488 are a series of small, shallow levels whose entrance can be located on the fern-covered slope east of Charlotte United's engine house. These can be explored in relative safety and are a good example of small-scale mining in a somewhat isolated area.

Plate 20:  *Wheal Coates — Towanroath Shaft*

# WHEAL COATES

D.  1815–1912

L.  1 mile S of St Agnes Head SW700501

M/O.  335 tons copper; 717 tons tin

S.  These well known industrial relics are finely situated on the magnificent cliffs near Chapel Porth. Ironically, the mine was a poor producer of both tin and copper. The 60″ pumping engine house on Towanroath Shaft was restored by the National Trust

44

in 1973, and renovation work on the stamps engine house was undertaken in 1986. The small building next to the stamps housed the whim. There are two stacks on the site, and several ruined buildings all connected with dressing to be found near the coastal footpath to St. Agnes. At low tide, the workings of Towanroath Shaft can be viewed in the roof of a large sea cave, where the course of the lode is clearly visible in the roof.

## TREVAUNANCE
D.　　1843–1887
L.　　½ mile W of St. Agnes SW712409
M/O.　1,960 tons copper; 550 tons tin
S.　　The engine house of this mine which once stood beside the coastal road below St. Agnes Beacon was demolished in 1984. Only the foundation walls of this building remain, together with a tall stack.

## POLBERRO
D.　　1837–1895
L.　　½ mile W of St. Agnes SW714515

Plate 21:　*Polberro — Turnavore Shaft*

45

M/O.    4,310 tons tin; 1,598 tons copper; some pyrites

S.    A well preserved 60″ pumping engine house, still roofed, stands on Turnavore Shaft. A stack and remains of the dressing floors are nearby. Main adit has its portal on Trevaunance Beach but it is unwise to enter it due to the constant flow of water issuing from the mouth.

## WHEAL FRIENDLY

D.    1860–1915

L.    St. Agnes SW720512

M/O.    450 tons copper; 440 tons tin

S.    The familiar 60″ pumping engine house of this relatively unproductive mine is in good condition, standing on high ground overlooking Trevaunance Coombe.

## WEST KITTY

D.    1879–1916

L.    St. Agnes SW718508

M/O.    10,076 tons tin; 185 tons copper

S.    A large pumping engine house stands virtually near the centre of the village itself, slightly west of the road to Perranporth. The whim engine house on Thomas section of the mine, at SW716511, was demolished in 1983. At SW733506, near the head of the Jericho Valley, are the ruined walls of part of the stamps used by this mine.

## WHEAL LUNA

D.    Early 1800's

L.    St. Agnes SW721517

M/O.    No records — tin

S.    The cavernous excavations and old men's levels of this long forgotten mine riddle the cliffs near the now submerged St. Agnes harbour. Most of these are accessible and safe to explore.

## WHEAL KITTY

D.    1834–1930

L.    ½ mile NE of St. Agnes SW724513

M/O.    13,121 tons tin; 2,024 tons copper

S.    The 65″ pumping engine house on Sara's Shaft stands amidst extensive dumps on high ground north of Trevaunance Cove. The dressing floors are now mostly overgrown with gorse, although some out-buildings and two chimney stacks dating from the later period of operation still stand. Several levels and adits can be seen in the cliff face below the main workings.

## GOONINNIS
D.     1860–1910
L.     East of St. Agnes SW726504
M/O.  No recorded output — tin
S.     An imposing 50″ pumping engine house and a small stack stand on what proved to be an unproductive trial for tin on the extensions of Wheal Kitty's lodes.

## POLBREEN (NEW WHEAL KITTY)
D.     1840–1899
L.     St. Agnes SW719503
M/O.  520 tons tin; 250 tons copper
S.     The ruined engine house of this small mine was once a familiar landmark seen to the west of the road leading into the village, but was demolished in 1971. Only a few scattered dumps remain.

## BLUE HILLS
D.     1813–1898
L.     $\frac{3}{4}$ mile NE of St. Agnes SW728516
M/O.  2,117 tons tin; some arsenic
S.     A small pumping engine house stands at the seaward end of Trevellas Coombe. There are extensive workings on both sides of the valley, including two stacks, remains of walls and wheel pits. Main adit discharges onto the beach but is now blocked with debris and flooded.

## CLIGGA HEAD
L.     $1\frac{1}{4}$ miles W of Perranporth SW738538
S.     The cliffs between St. Agnes and Perranporth are pitted with old men's workings; these are the traces left of past generations of miners that have scoured this area for copper and other minerals whose multi-coloured lodes stain the awesome chasms which are a feature along this stretch of coastline. Cligga Head has been

prospected over sporadic periods for centuries, and the concrete foundations at the top of the cliff date from a re-working in the 1930's. Middle level, some 80 ft. from the cliff bottom, can be reached by negotiating the old miner's hazardous route down a gully in the cliff face, in which old rail tracks are embedded. This opens out into a complex series of levels and winzes, and a great deal of caution is needed when exploring these mine workings, which were recently being prospected once again.

## DROSKYN, PERRAN UNITED and GREAT ST. GEORGE

L.  $\frac{1}{4}$ mile W of Perranporth

S.  From Cligga Head to Droskyn Point, the cliff faces are honeycombed wth the burrowings left from this group of ancient copper producers. A particularly awesome man-made cavern, with passages leading off from it, can be reached by a cliff path at SW751542; a shaft here connects with a level at the base of the cliff. At Droskyn Point, the cliffs are riddled with levels and adits, some of which can be explored at low tide. The natural looking arches of Chapel Rock are, in fact, man-made from the numerous tunnelings of the old miners dating as far back as the 18th century.

## BUDNICK CONSOLS and WHEAL ROSE

D.  1832–1904

L.  $\frac{1}{4}$ mile E of Perranporth SW765542

M/O.  1,100 tons tin; 300 tons lead; 210 tons copper; 2,470 tons zinc; some silver

S.  A single stack stands at the entrance to the Perranporth Camping Site near Reen Manor. Beside the stack, an adit discharges water into a culvert; a large shaft dump lies in a field behind the camp site. Wheal Rose worked with this mine, and its site today is identifiable by a run of gorse-covered burrows and filled-in shafts at the top of the hill at SW773547, in the vicinity of Rose Village.

## PRINCE ROYAL

D.  1825–1890

L.  $1\frac{1}{4}$ miles S of Perranporth SW748521

M/O.  495 tons copper; 5 tons tin

S.      There are scattered waste tips over the hillside beside the track leading to Trevellas. The ruins of a dry are at the foot of the hill beside the road, slightly south of Carnbargus.

## PERRAN WHEAL ALFRED
D.      1820–1860
L.      1½ miles S of Perranporth SW750515
M/O.      No records — silver and lead
S.      The only remains left from this unproductive trial are two large slatey burrows either side of the road east of Blowinghouse.

## WHEAL MITHIAN
D.      1811–1838
L.      2 miles S of Perranporth SW748503
M/O.      No records — copper
S.      A large shaft dump can be seen adjacent to the abandoned railway line south east of Mithian Farm. Several ruined and decaying buildings, including a dry and ore-treatment shed, lie in a small wood at SW746508 — these may be connected with this mine and others that have worked in the Perrancombe Valley.

## LAMBRIGGEN (SOUTH ST. GEORGE)
D.      circa 1840's, re-opened in 1927
L.      1¾ miles S of Perranporth SW761511
M/O.      No records — lead and copper
S.      A fenced shaft of large proportions and extensive tips are next to a small wood south of Golla Farm. There are two other shafts in the surrounding fields, also both fenced off.

## WEST SHEPHERDS
D.      1840–1851
L.      1¼ miles S of Perranporth SW759518
M/O.      No records — unproductive trial for silver and lead
S.      A single shaft and overgrown dumps from this old sett lie in dense undergrowth at the northern end of Bice's Wood.

## PERRAN WHEAL JANE and SOUTH WHEAL LEISURE
D.      1830–1870, re-worked 1911 and 1930
L.      ¾ mile SE of Perranporth SW759528

M/O.    Small amounts of tin

S.      Old, unproductive mines working copper, lead and tin lodes on the west side of the Penwartha Valley. A few pits, grassed-over mounds, broken walls and a large opencast quarry near the track from Penwartha to Liskey are all that remain.

## TREAMBLE
D.      1859–1892, prospected in the 1930's and 1940's

L.      2 miles N of Perranporth SW780564

M/O.    15,300 tons haematite; 32 tons lead

S.      A small chimney stack survives in the sand dune area near Mount; most of the dumps are now overgrown. An ore treatment building and dressing floors can be found in the valley below at SW786560.

## TREBISKEN AND TREBELLAN (WHEAL CUBERT)
D.      1846–1864

L.      ½ mile S of Cubert SW785571

M/O.    1,140 tons lead; 6,500 oz silver

S.      The workings of this old group of lead mines now lie hidden amongst gorse and thickets on the valley side west of Trebellan hamlet, overlooking the Holywell stream.

## PERU
D.      1820–1829

L.      1 mile SE of Cubert SW795564

M/O.    No records — silver and lead. Later included in the Duchy Peru sett

S.      The ruins of a small engine house and stack, one of the oldest structures of its kind in Cornwall, with a shaft and dump, stand on the south bank of the Holywell stream adjacent to the disused Treamble–Shepherds branch railway line.

Dir.    Take the minor road from Treworthen Farm to Rejerrah. At the fifth field on the left, a small track leads north. Walk up this track into the field, turn left into the next field and proceed upwards over the ridge, using the spire of Cubert Church as a guide. Drop down towards the railway track, now enveloped in trees and gorse bushes. The stack of the engine house can be seen protruding above the treeline. A gap in the fence allows access to the embankment, and the mine itself. To stand on the site of this ancient prospect is to experience the aura of metal mining which seems to surround small workings such as this.

## DUCHY PERU
D.    1858–1886
L.    1½ miles SE of Cubert SW796556
M/O.    21,000 tons haematitie; 20,000 tons zinc; 11,000 tons mixed haematite; 180 tons ochre
S.    One of the richest mines in the area, Duchy Peru's extensive dumps and shafts are scattered over the fields south of Rejerrah. The base walls of an engine house are on the edge of one shaft near Saddle Rock Farm. On the Perran Iron Lode, which this mine exploited, there is a large quarry at SW788558 in the Treamble Valley. Smaller quarries between this and Mount belong to the workings of HALWYN, MOUNT and SOUTH MOUNT. All were prospected in the 1940's for silver and lead, without much success.

## GREAT RETALLACK
D.    1858–1880
L.    1¼ miles SE of Cubert SW791560
M/O.    10,800 tons zinc; 200 tons lead; 600 oz silver
S.    Although badly damaged by the military in a demolition exercise in the 1950's, a fate which befell many such buildings during that period, the remains of the pumping engine house, reduced to the base walls, still stand on the site, east of North Treamble Farm.

## NEW CHIVERTON
D.    1864–1878
L.    1 mile SW of Goonhavern SW773529
M/O.    300 tons lead; 1,300 oz silver; 640 tons zinc; 25 tons arsenic
S.    A large but now decaying pumping engine house stands in the valley beside the Perranwell–Bolingey footpath, and adjacent to the old Newquay rail viaduct.

## WEST CHIVERTON
D.    1859–1886
L.    1¾ miles S of Goonhavern SW793508
M/O.    45,100 tons lead; 22,000 tons zinc; 1,221,200 oz silver

Plate 22:  *West Chiverton*

S.     The richest of the Chiverton Group, West Chiverton's sett is marked today by Batter's finely preserved three-storied pumping engine house, on waste ground near the lane leading to Higher Ventongimps Farm. There are also some extensive tailings and ruined walls on the site of the stamps and dressing floors, although the stamps engine house was dynamited in 1952.

## CHIVERTON MOOR (GREAT CALLESTOCK MOOR)

D.     1847–1873
L.     2 miles S of Goonhavern SW785503
M/O.     2,240 tons lead; 24,000 oz silver
S.     The bob wall of an engine house still stands on the sett, at the edge of a small wood a short distance north of Chynhale Farm.

## EAST WHEAL ROSE

D.     1834–1885
L.     $\frac{3}{4}$ mile SE of Newlyn East SW839558
M/O.     48,200 tons lead; 212,700 oz silver; 280 tons zinc; 160 tons copper

S.      Impressive from any viewpoint, the massively constructed and still roofed 100″ pumping engine house on North Wheal Rose Shaft, with its separate 100 ft. stack, dominates the flat marshy basin formed by Newlyn Downs. Without doubt, the grandest relic of its type in Cornwall.

Dir.   A major part of this site has now been taken over by the Lappa Valley scheme, whereby a single-track railway ferries tourists up to the mine at a cost. Several flooded shafts and a caved-in gunnis can be seen in the vicinity of the engine house; North Wheal Rose Shaft itself is flooded to the collar, and a nearby level, heavily timbered, leading into the hillside has been boarded up. For non-paying visitors, take the Mitchell–Newlyn East road from the A30 for a mile, then walk across the field-cum-rubbish tip towards the mine, which offers a fine view with the wooded Downs as a backdrop. Behind, covering the whole of the southern slopes of Newlyn Downs, are the waste tips and shafts of the original Wheal Rose and East Rose workings, and other smaller lead prospects which became swallowed up when the mine was in operation.

## NEWQUAY CLIFF WORKINGS

S.      Between SW810618, Tolcarne, and SW824625, Lusty Glaze, the relatively low cliffs at Newquay are, in some places, honeycombed with the old men's levels and adits of several ancient mines that prospected the area for copper and lead without much success during the years 1830–1870. Among these were NEWQUAY SILVER LEAD MINE, TOLCARNE, WHEAL NARROW, ROSECLIFFE and NEW WHEAL ROSE, the latter being an amalgamation of the whole group. Nothing remains from these mines inland, only the aforementioned cliff workings giving any indication of past mining activity in this now built up area.

# Truro — St. Austell

## CARNON STREAM MINE

D.     1822–1830

L.      ½ mile SE of Devoran SW802388

M/O.  No records — tin lodes under the stream bed.

S.      A ruinous, decaying engine house, virtually only one wall intact, stands on the bank of Tallack's Creek — with Peru Mine, one of the oldest industrial relics surviving in Cornwall.

## CROW HILL MINE

D.   1831–1869
L.   3½ miles E of Ladock SW938509
M/O.   475 tons lead; 2,903 oz silver
S.   A very smally-constructed engine house, the stump of a stack and a burrow are on the east side of the valley above the River Fal, best viewed from the Trenowth railway viaduct, although the site has become much overgrown by trees and undergrowth in recent years.

## CHYPRAZE CONSOLS (TREFULLOCK)

D.   1844–1853
L.   3½ miles N of Ladock SW904563
M/O.   2½ tons tin
S.   A solitary chimney stack stands in a wood at the entrance to the lane leading to Burthy Row, on what was little more than an unproductive tin trial.

## ST. AUSTELL CONSOLS

D.   1846–1879
L.   2 miles SE of St. Stephen SW967512
M/O.   75 tons copper; 1,074 tons tin; 2½ tons lead; small quantities of arsenic, cobalt, nickel and uranium
S.   A tall, graceful chimney stack stands amidst extensive waste tips and shafts between Trewithien Lane End and Downderry.

## GREAT DOWGAS

D.   1838–1907
L.   1½ miles SE of St. Stephen SW963514
M/O.   129 tons tin; 4 tons cobalt; several tons ochre
S.   Another single chimney stack adjoining the sett of St. Austell Consols, overlooking the china clay tips near St. Stephen.

## VENTONWYN

D.   1903–1907
L.   1 mile W of Sticker SW962504
M/O.   138 tons tin

S.      A very conspicuous stamps engine house and separate stack is on high ground north of the A390 road to St. Austell, and visible from great distances to the south.

## SOUTH POLGOOTH

D.      1830–1882
L.      ½ mile SW of Polgooth SW989499
M/O.    149 tons tin
S.      A large pumping engine house in good condition stands on a ridge above Sticker, on Treloweth Common. Adjacent to the engine house is a calciner of some considerable size, partly enveloped in ivy.

Plate 23:    *South Polgooth*

## GREAT POLGOOTH

D.      1800–1885
L.      North east of Polgooth Village SX001504
M/O.    3,000 tons tin; 595 tons copper
S.      The shell of the pumping engine house on Taylor's Shaft is a familiar sight at the edge of what now forms part of a golf course, above the village. This has recently (1986) been

55

renovated. The stamps engine house is situated at the foot of the hill in undergrowth with part of its roof intact.

## TREGREHAN CONSOLS (WHEAL ELIZA)
D.     1889–1909
L.     1½ miles E of St. Austell SX046532
M/O.   13½ tons tin
S.     Once a conspicuous object from the A390 into St. Blazey, the pumping engine house and stack of this small tin producer is now in a very decayed state and virtually hidden by trees and undergrowth in a small wood south east of Trenowah Farm.

## FOWEY CONSOLS
D.     1813–1869
L.     1 mile NE of St. Blazey SX083558
M/O.   319,700 tons copper; 2,287 tons pyrites
S.     Austen's 80″ pumping engine house is a well known relic on high ground overlooking Tywardreath Highway. There are some extensive dumps on the site, and another large engine house wreathed in ivy next to the stream in the valley below at SX091559.

## WHEAL GASSON (PENROSE)
D.     circa 1840's
L.     ½ mile N of St. Dennis SW948593
M/O.   No records — small quantities of alluvial tin and copper
S.     A small stamps engine house stands on Goss Moor, near Penrose Veor Farm, erected in 1846 to treat ore and alluvial material from neighbouring prospects. The top portion of the stack is missing, and some grassed-over burrows can be traced over the surrounding moor.

## PAR CONSOLS
D.     1841–1869
L.     ¼ mile W of Par SX072533
M/O.   122,689 tons copper; 3,785 tons tin; 940 tons zinc
S.     Of this prolific group of mines to have worked in the Par area, only the ivy-covered bob wall of an engine house remains today, near the track leading to the Mount Inn holiday camp. The rest of the workings are now obscured by thick undergrowth.

Plate 24: *Bob wall — Par Consols*

# St. Austell — Bodmin — Liskeard

## BELOWDA HILL MINE
D.     1872–1902, re-worked 1935
L.     1½ miles NW of Roche SW966616
M/O.  53 tons tin; small quantities of wolfram
S.     A small pumping engine house in good condition, with a nearby boiler house, stands prominently on a ridge to the north of the A30, overlooking Goss Moor.

## GREAT ROYALTON
D.     1859–1901
L.     1 mile N of Roche SW977617
M/O.  143 tons tin
S.     One of the many small tin producers to have worked on the granite slopes of Belowda Beacon, Great Royalton's site today is marked by a single chimney stack, boiler house and ore-processing plant, all in ruins, near the road to Demelza.

57

Plate 25: *Belowda Hill Mine*

## BRYNN TYE
D.    1833–1871
L.    1¼ miles N of Roche SW982625
M/O.  18 tons tin
S.    A single stack and the fragmentary remains (part of one wall) of the engine house stand on fern-covered moorland near Belowda Beacon and Little Brynn, a short distance north-east of Great Royalton Mine.

## LANJEW
D.    1853–1859
L.    ½ mile W of Withiel SW986653
M/O.  2,390 tons haematite
S.    A small, well preserved chimney stack is still standing on the site of this mine which exploited an iron lode. It is situated in the corner of a steeply sloping field directly north of Lanjew Farm, above the valley.

## TREGOLLAN AND TRETOIL

D.     1839–1882

L.     1¾ miles S of Bodmin SX067641

M/O.   24,913 tons copper; 49 tons tin; 12 tons lead; 8,378 tons iron; 156 tons zinc

S.     These two mines were an amalgamation of several old copper producers that worked the deep valleys south of Bodmin. Two stacks, one shrouded in ivy, are situated on the edge of a small wood slightly east of Tregullan. Another stack and miner's dry can be located north of Tretoil Farm.

## BOCONNOC AND GREY MARE

D.     1853–1858

L.     1¼ mile NE of Restormel Bridge SX129628

M/O.   Small quantities of iron ore

S.     This long forgotten prospect is identifiable today by the foundations walls of possibly an engine house, an overgrown dump and a collapsed shaft issuing a stream of ochrous water in Iron Mine Plantation, east of Respryn Bridge.

## WHEAL GLYNN (HURTSTOCKS WOOD MINE)

D.     1854–1864

L.     1¼ miles S of Cardinham SX111675

M/O.   18 tons lead

S.     The ruins of the pumping engine house with castellated stack, shaft and collapsed adit can still be found in Hurtstocks Wood.

Dir.    Until recently, this relic, buried deep in forestry plantation land that overall forms the Cardinham Woodlands, was very difficult to find. However, a nature trail has now been blazed through the gorge-like valleys that separate Hurtstocks, Deviock and Callabarrett Woods, and a signpost marked 'silver mine' takes one up the track past the engine house, which is still obscured from view by conifers. Because of the geographical nature of these valleys, it is still a long trek to visit Wheal Glynn.

## WHEAL MARY

D.     1860–1880

L.     St. Neot SX187674

M/O.   144 tons tin; 150 tons copper; 80 tons lead; small quantities of silver and arsenic

S.        There are some scattered dumps near Coombe House and a square calciner stack on the side of the valley at Lampen, SX184673. This dates from a re-working of the burrows in the early 1900's. The dumps and burrows to the east of the road at SX194676 are those of WHEAL SISTERS whose sett was amalgamated with Wheal Mary in 1849.

## NORTHWOOD

D.      circa 1870's

L.      $2\frac{1}{4}$ miles NE of St. Neot SX201698

M/O.  2 tons tin in 1875

S.        The gaunt remains of a stamps engine house, erected to treat ore from neighbouring prospects, stand on the southern slope of Northwood Downs, very much off the beaten track. In 1986, some renovation work was being undertaken on this site. Lower down the road, in the garden of a house near the turn off to West Northwood, is a small stack that at one time also worked with Northwood.

Dir.    Take the road east from St. Neot, past Wenmouth Cross, towards Draynes. At SX204680, turn left and proceed north. It's a long uphill haul for a mile or so towards the Downs, with the engine house north of West Northwood Farm.

## HERODSFOOT and NORTH HERODSFOOT

D.      1844–1884

L.      3 miles S of Liskeard SX212604

M/O.  19,102 tons lead; 617,264 oz silver; 17 tons copper

S.        A small engine house, boiler house and stack can be located in a valley to the west of the village. Two more engine houses, in a poor state of preservation, and another stack are a short distance south of the village near Homehill Wood.

## TREBEIGH (NORTH WREY AND JULIA)

D.      1858–1881

L.      1 mile NW of St. Ive Cross SX302679

M/O.  10 cwt of silver

S.        The ivy-covered bob wall of the engine house, some overgrown dumps and a shaft can be seen in a corner of a field west of the hamlet of Gang.

## WHEAL TRELAWNEY

D.     1840–1884

L.     2¼ miles E of Liskeard SX288643

M/O.  23,180 tons lead; 290 tons pyrites; 7,320 tons mispickel; 460 tons arsenic; 680,740 oz silver

S.     A finely proportioned chimney stack dominates the landscape near Trehane crossroads. Further down the steep hill towards Menheniot, there are some extensive workings on the right of the road at SX286636, including an ivy-covered stack.

## WREY AND LUDCOTT UNITED
## (includes NORTH TRELAWNEY)

D.     1852–1866

L.     3 miles E of Liskeard SX297659

M/O.  10,505 tons lead; 294,410 oz silver

Site &  The extensive workings of this group of lead producers lie in
Dir.    Westdown Wood, adjoining Woodfield Farm. The site is reached by proceeding down the track from Butterdon Mill past the farm. Cross over the stream, a tributary of the River Tiddy; a steep climb to the left brings you to the wood. Several shafts, a leat, two water-wheel pits and the stump of a stack can be located on the densely vegetated slopes either side of the stream. On the northern edge of the wood, near the fields that drop down to the farm, are a group of old buldings in a very ruinous state, comprising the walls of two engine houses, a boiler house and a tall, ivy-covered chimney stack.

# Caradon Hill

## SOUTH CARADON

D.     1837–1885

L.     South west slope of Caradon Hill SX266698

M/O.  217,820 tons copper

S.     Large scale workings covering the southern slopes of Caradon Hill north of the villages of Darite and Crow's Nest mark the site of this, the richest of the Caradon Copper mines. Kittow's Shaft (SX274699) exhibits the remains of two engine houses, two stacks and an enormous burrow. Slightly west, an ivy-shrouded engine house with separate stack stands on Jope's Shaft. There are the ruins of three more engine houses north of Jope's Shaft, on the western side of the valley above the Caradon Stream, with traces of the mines' dressing floors in the valley itself. The course of the long abandoned Liskeard–Caradon railway can still be traced, circling the hill in the direction of the Phoenix United Group near Minions.

## WEST CARADON
D.      1837–1886
L.      ¾ mile S of Minions SX263701
M/O.    91,995 tons copper
S.      The vast burrows and waste tips of this mine, amongst the most extensive in Cornwall, take up the whole of the valley side to Gonamena. One engine house stack survives amidst all the rubble.

## GONAMENA
D.      1844–1871
L.      ½ mile S of Minions SX263705
M/O.    9,985 tons copper; 10 tons tin
S.      One of the less productive copper mines in this moorland area, Gonamena's sett today is identifiable by one engine house wall and a large dump situated at the head of the Caradon Valley.

## CRADDOCK MOOR
D.      1844–1873
L.      ¾ mile S of Minions SX256701
M/O.    20,080 tons copper
S.      A smally constructed, ruined engine house and stack stands on barren moorland west of West Caradon Mine. Another chimney stack also stands on the site, along with piles of 'deads'.

## WEST PHOENIX
D.      1851–1875
L.      ½ mile NW of Minions SX256720
M/O.    308 tons tin
S.      A small engine house and stack is on moorland adjoining the Withey Brook and south west of the Cheesewring Quarry.

## SOUTH PHOENIX

D.     1847–1892

L.      $\frac{3}{4}$ mile NE of Minions SX263715

M/O.   419 tons tin

S.      The mines' 50″ pumping engine house is in good condition but presents a rather odd appearance as the bob wall has been built up during the time that the building was used as a dwelling.

## PHOENIX UNITED

D.     1848–1898

L      $\frac{3}{4}$ mile NE of Minions SX268718

M/O.   16,352 tons tin; 82,686 tons copper

S.      On this site stands the finely preserved 80″ pumping engine house on Prince of Wales Shaft, with its distinctive square-based stack. The ruins of Hamilton's 26″ pumping engine house, now reduced to two crumbling walls, are beside the Minions–Henwood road at SX264718

## WHEAL JENKIN

D.     1830–1890

Plate 26:    *Wheal Jenkin*

63

L.     East of Minions SX266712

M/O.  292 tons tin

S.     The two granite engine houses of this unproductive tin mine, one of which is in a very ruinous state and has a separate stack, stand at over 1,000 ft. above sea level on the north slope of Caradon Hill. Near this mine is the abandoned tramline that descends the hill and connects with the workings of Marke Valley at Upton Cross.

## MARKE VALLEY

D.     1837–1890

L.     $\frac{1}{4}$ mile S of Upton Cross SX279717

M/O.  128,500 tons copper; 393 tons tin

S.     Two engine houses, one wreathed in ivy, a single stack and extensive dumps stand in a picturesque group on the north east slope of Caradon Hill. The ivy-covered stump of another stack can be seen on the side of the valley east of the B3254 to Liskeard at SX282718.

## GLASGOW CARADON CONSOLS
## (TOKENBURY AND YOLLAND CONSOLS)

D.     1841–1884

L.     1 mile S of Upton Cross SX277703

M/O.  37,500 tons copper

S.     There are no surface buildings remaining from this mine; the most conspicuous feature is a mountainous dump beside the road to Liskeard, slightly south west of Caradon Villa.

# Callington — Gunnislake

## WHEAL GOULD (COLQUITE/SOUTH CALLINGTON)

D.     1844–1870

L.     $1\frac{1}{4}$ miles S of Callington SX357677

M/O   38 tons pyrites; 3,391 tons arsenic

S.     This small mine worked on the wooded banks of the stream that flows from Newbridge. A 30 ft. high stack stands on the edge of the wood, and nearby are the walls of an old dry, the main engine shaft and a quarry used for building material.

Dir.   Take the road south from Callington towards Amytree crossroads. Where the road crosses the stream at SX361678, turn right and skirt the stream bank for $\frac{1}{4}$ mile — there is no path or track here, so the route can be wet. The mine is midway in the wood south of Colquite Farm.

## BLOGSTERS (PRIDE OF THE EAST/WEST REDMOOR)

D.     Earlier dates unknown. Re-worked 1928–1934
L.     1$\frac{1}{4}$ miles NW of Callington SX345707
M/O.   No records — some tin
S.     Old opencuts, shafts and flooded levels are in a wooded ravine south of Whitley Farm. A tall chimney stack and the remains of some calciners, dating from an earlier period of operation, are also on the site.
Dir.   This is another unknown mining venture that is off the beaten track. Take the road from Redmoor Cottage (SX352711) to Callington, turn right towards Haye and take the track to the right that heads north west. This leads into a wood that eventually drops into a valley near 'ford' on the O/S map. Go up the path towards Whitley Farm — just before reaching the outbuildings, turn left, cross over the stream into another wooded valley. The workings of the mine, hidden amongst trees on rising ground, are on the right.

## COMBLAWN MINE (SMITH'S VENTURE)

D.     1845–1874
L.     1 mile W of Callington SX346695
M/O.   25 tons tin
S.     These old mines exploited lead lodes on the eastern slopes of the valley south of Haye under various names without much success. A few scattered dumps and crumbling walls, with one or two shafts, can be found amongst dense vegetation down the valley to Pidgerton Wood.

## REDMOOR

D.     1861–1908
L.     1 mile N of Callington SX357711
M/O.   148 tons tin; 47 tons copper; 190 tons arsenic; 8 tons silver ore; 9,170 oz silver; 2 tons wolfram
S.     Wantonly demolished without permission in 1983, the pumping and whim engine houses of this mine, with their separate stack, are now nothing more than a pile of rubble. Only the base walls of one engine house remains.

## HOLMBUSH and EAST HOLMBUSH

D.     1822–1892

L.     $\frac{1}{4}$ mile N of Kelly Bray SX358721

M/O.  42,900 tons copper; 1,689 tons lead; 20,093 oz silver; 20,326 tons mispickel; 10,554 tons arsenic

S.     Three engine houses and a stack stand in a compact group near Holmbush Plantation, adjoining the Stoke Climsland road. A large, roofed engine house in the valley below, now partly covered in ivy, marks the site of the less productive East Holmbush Mine.

Plate 28:   *Stamps/Crusher engine house — New Consols*

## NEW CONSOLS (WHEAL MARTHA)

D.     1844–1888, re-worked 1915 and 1943

L.     Luckett, $1\frac{1}{2}$ miles N of Kit Hill SX387736

M/O.  28,682 tons copper; 735 tons tin; 3,587 tons arsenic; 2 tons wolfram; 3,779 tons pyrites; 3,575 tons mispickel

S.     A mine at the northern edge of Kit Hill that produced a wide variety of ores without too much success. A large engine house clad in ivy stands on Broadgate's Shaft near the road to Lidwell. On the same ridge further east at Luckett is the massive shell of

Phillip's 80″ pumping engine house; below, situated amidst extensive dumps, is the 24″ crusher house. All three buildings are still roofed, but fast becoming obscured by dense vegetation. The whim house which used to stand near the crusher house was demolished in the 1970's. Arsenic flues, calciners and two more stacks can be seen on the steep hillside south of the village towards Monkscross.

## WHEAL TOM
D.    1850–1852
L.    $\frac{3}{4}$ mile SW of Luckett SX377729
M/O.  No records — tin and wolfram
S.    The ruins of a small engine house, shaft, opencuts and the stump of a stack can be located in a small wood bordering the Deerpark Valley between Newmill Ford and Clitters.

## DEERPARK MINE
D.    1850–1875
L.    $\frac{3}{4}$ mile NE of Luckett SX392729
M/O.  $1\frac{1}{2}$ tons tin in 1873
S.    A tall, ivy-clad chimney stack, resembling a giant green pipe cleaner, is a conspicuous object east of the steep hill that descends into Luckett. There are also some ruined walls on the site, at the edge of the wood adjoining the Greenscombe Valley.

## EXCELSIOR TUNNEL
D.    1877–1938
L.    1 mile SW of Luckett SX381724
S.    A costly and ultimately unsuccesful attempt to drive a tunnel through the granite of Kit Hill in the hope of discovering new and unworked tin lodes. The portal is barred by an iron grid-cum-gate but access is still possible, although in view of the state of the single passeway ($\frac{1}{2}$ mile in length), undesirable.
Dir.   Take the road from Monkscross to Luckett and turn left down the track towards 'Clitters'. This descends rapidly into the Deerpark Valley. An old outbuilding can be found amongst thick scrub, with some scattered dumps. The tunnel entrance is on the left of the track near this building, obscured by trees and brambles.

## SILVERHILL MINE

D.     1881–1883

L.     1 mile E of Callington SX377696

S.     Like the Excelsior Tunnel, an abortive and short lived attempt to burrow into Kit Hill from the south in the hope of cross-cutting lodes earlier worked by Silver Valley and Wheal Langford. There are extensive waste tips adjacent to the stream west of Fullaford Cottages and a stream of ochrous water issuing from the blocked-up tunnel mouth itself. Another tunnel entrance can be located in the bank of a low cliff south of the road at SX374695.

## WHEAL LANGFORD (WHEAL BROTHERS)

D.     1824–1890

L.     $1\frac{1}{4}$ miles E of Callington SX383695

M/O.  79 tons lead; 10 tons manganese; 25 tons zinc; $3\frac{1}{2}$ tons silver ore; 2,530 oz silver

S.     A large pumping engine house with a separate stack stands south of the road and east of Fullaford Cottages. The whim is completely enveloped in ivy and is situated near a flooded shaft. Another pumping engine house, hidden partly by trees, stands on waste ground at the road junction near Mount Lodge. An interesting feature of this building is the incline entrance to the shaft which is approached from within the engine house below the bob wall.

## SILVER VALLEY

D.     1815–1855; prospected in 1912–1918 and 1943

L.     $1\frac{1}{2}$ miles E of Callington SX384700

M/O.  9 tons lead; small quantities of Wolfram.

S.     Two well preserved stacks stand in the valley which has been landscaped in recent years. One is situated midway down, the other nearer Mount Lodge. Two or three shafts and some scattered dumps can be seen between the two chimneys.

## WEST PRINCE OF WALES

D.     1900–1908

L.     $\frac{3}{4}$ mile NW of Harrowbarrow SX389706

M/O.  9 tons tin; 3 tons arsenic

S.     A tall and imposing chimney stack stands in a deep valley to the south of Sevenstones. The walls of another old building, possibly a dry, can be located at the top of the valley next to the track leading to West Harrowbarrow.

## SOUTH KIT HILL
D.     1870–1883
L.     Southern slope of Kit Hill SX375709
M/O.  62 tons tin
S.     A tall granite stack on the slope of Kit Hill marks the site of this small tin producer. The whim engine house, which was still standing in 1976, has now been reduced to a pile of rubble by successive gales.

## KIT HILL CONSOLS
D.     1860–1890
L.     Kit Hill summit SX375713
M/O.  139 tons tin; 15 tons copper; 125 tons wolfram; 2 tons arsenic
S.     The 80 ft. high ornamented stack of this mine, situated at the top of the hill and festooned with ariels, is probably the best known industrial monument in NE Cornwall. Several small levels can be found penetrating the hillside in the vicinity of the stack.

## EAST KIT HILL
D.     1853–1909
L.     $\frac{3}{4}$ mile E of Kit Hill Mine SX389711
M/O.  218 tons tin; 2 tons arsenic
S.     A small stamps engine house in a ruined state, stack and boiler house form a picturesque group near the track leading to Kit Hill from the east. The site was also used by Kit Hill Mine for the treatment of tin ore.

## PRINCE OF WALES
D.     1865–1914
L.     Harrowbarrow SX401705
M/O.  10,845 tons copper; 1,102 tons tin; 23 tons lead; 20 tons silver ore; several thousand tons of pyrites
S.     The very extensive workings of this mine are on either side of the road leading into the village from the east. Three engine houses stand on the site, the pumping house on Watson's Shaft being

Plate 29:  *East Kit Hill*

the best preserved. Near these relics are the remains of the milling plant and two stacks. The chimney stack that can be seen lower down in the valley at SX404700 marks the site of the Coombe Arsenic Works, abandoned in the 1920's.

## HINGSTON DOWN CONSOLS

D.     1850–1917

L.     $1\frac{1}{2}$ miles W of Gunnislake SX411713

M/O.    65,710 tons copper; 254 tons tin; 200 tons arsenic; 152 tons wolfram

S.     The pumping engine house on Bayly's Shaft is in a good state of preservation, with the flat-parapet roof intact and iron frames still showing in the window openings. The two stacks that flanked this building on the granite ridge north of the A390 road were demolished in 1982. Some concrete masonry from the later period of working still remains.

Plate 27: *Hingston Down Consols*

## GREYSTONE SILVER-LEAD MINE

D.   1831–1880
L.   3 miles SE of Launceston SX359804
M/O.  A few cwt of lead ore
S.   The pumping engine house and separate stack of this small lead prospect still stand on the site, at the edge of a wood west of Greystone Bridge. Both buildings are now, however, in a very dilapidated state and almost obscured by a thick tangle of undergrowth and trees.

## WHEAL SOPHIA (MODITONHAM AND MARRABOROUGH CONSOLS)

D.   1846–1852
L.   1 mile E of Botus Fleming SX419615
M/O.  No records — copper and lead
S.   Although this mine lies outside the Gunnislake area, it is included because of its surviving chimney stack which stands in a field overlooking a tidal creek of the Tamar. This small stack is the only mining relic left to be seen in the Saltash district.

71

# North West Cornwall

## TREGORDEN
D.    1848–1852
L.    1 mile NE of Wadebridge SX001737
M/O.  78 tons lead
S.    The site of this small lead producer is identifiable today by a tall chimney stack and a few scattered dumps in a wood slightly south of Tregorden Farm. This is best reached by taking the track north from Ball off the A39 which leads up to the wood where the workings lie.

## TREROOSEL and WHITEWELL (TREBURGETT UNITED)
D.    circa 1850's
L.    ½ mile W of St. Teath SX057808
M/O.  No records — silver and lead
S.    The ruined walls of a smally constructed engine house and a line of shaft burrows survive from this unproductive group, in a field to the south of Treroosel Farm. More dumps and overgrown burrows can be seen further south at Whitewell.

## OLD TREBURGETT
D.    1817–1881
L.    ¾ mile SW of St. Teath SX057797
M/O.  2,180 tons lead; 9,530 oz silver; 44 tons zinc; 62 tons iron; 120 tons pyrites
S.    The bob wall of one engine house is still on the property, with extensive waste tips and several shafts in the vicinity of Treburgett Farm, south of the B3267.

## WHEAL SARAH
D.    1843–1858
L.    1¾ miles N of St. Kew SX036791
M/O.  No records — an unsuccessful trial for antimony
S.    The crumbling, ivy-covered shell of an engine house lies in dense thickets beside an enormous burrow, slightly east of Tregildern Farm.

## PENTIRE GLAZE AND PENTIRE UNITED

D.  1813–1857
L.  ¾ mile N of Polzeath SW941799
M/O.  955 tons lead; 19,065 oz silver; 136 tons copper
S.  This old group of mines were known to be working lead lodes in the cliffs at Pentire as far back as the 16th century. The site of their operations is marked today by the foundation walls of an engine house and stack, near the entrance to the cliff-top car park. There are some considerable dumps near this relic, with more tips and ruined walls in the valley below.

## TREGARDOCK

D.  1851–1868
L.  2¾ miles NW of St. Teath SX041839
M/O.  60 tons lead; 690 oz silver; some copper
S.  Another ancient lead mine that was in operation in the late 1500's. The base walls of a small engine house still survive on the verge of Tregardock Cliff, together with a grassed-over burrow and filled-in shaft.

## WHEAL BRAY

D.  1840–1858
L.  2 miles NW of Altarnun SX198823
M/O.  510 tons copper
S.  The remains of this mine, consisting of one engine house wall, one wall of another building, some overgrown dumps and several shafts, lie in the marshy valley between Bray and Carne Downs, on Bodmin Moor. The dumps here were treated for uranium by the Atomic Energy Authority in 1953, with little success.
Dir.  From the A30 at Fivelanes, take the road to Altarnun, then proceed in a westerly direction through Trekennick and Hurden towards Trebray. On the bend of the minor road that leads to this hamlet, a track veers off to the left, crossing a ford between the two downs. A path winds up the valley and the main workings are on the west bank of the stream.

# The Tamar Valley — Cornwall

The stretch of the Tamar Valley between the northern edge of Devon Great Consols and the tip of the Bere Alston Peninsula is for the most part negotiable, and the mines clustered on both sides of the river fairly easy to reach. The terrain is naturally hilly, as the contour lines drop steeply from the granite uplands of Kit Hill and the surrounding moors. Unfortunately, most of the mines of the Tamar are now in a poor state of preservation since the publication of Frank Booker's "Industrial Archaeology of the Tamar Valley" which details the area, and many remains are almost hidden from view by the dense vegetation that clings to any abandoned building and is a particular feature of the landscape in this rather isolated part of the country.

## DRAKEWALLS

D.  1817–1897
L.  ½ mile SW of Gunnislake SX426706
M/O.  5,433 tons tin; 2,015 tons copper; 2,638 tons arsenic
S.  Once a prominent sight at the top of the long hill that climbs out of Gunnislake, the mine's large stamps engine house was demolished in 1975, but the stump of its stack survives. The pumping engine house beside the road to Calstock is still standing, along with two more stacks shorn of their top portion of bricks, and one wall of another engine house, now surrounded by thickets and brambles. There are also extensive waste tips south of the road near the railway line.

## WHEAL BRAMBLE (SOUTH DEVON)

D.  1853–1898
L.  1 mile NW of Gunnislake SX418723
M/O.  234 tons mispickel
S.  This unproductive mine exploited lodes believed to emanate from Devon Great Consols on the opposite side of the river, without much success. A prominent chimney stack survives on the sett, together with the walls of the small engine house on Smee's Shaft whch lies in a nearby thicket.

## GREENHILL ARSENIC WORKS

L.  ¾ mile NW of Gunnislake SX418718
S.  The giant stone chimney stack of the arsenic works towers above

74

the village and is a landmark for miles around in this area. Another stack and the remains of flues and calciners also remain, near the road from Gunnislake to Chilsworthy.

## GUNNISLAKE CLITTERS
D.     1822–1908
L.     ½ mile NW of Gunnislake SX422723
M/O.  33,350 tons copper; 1,067 tons tin; 443 tons wolfram; 180 tons arsenic
S.     These workings cover the steep slope of Clitters Wood that descends to the river. Two engine houses and a separate, tall stack are near the road to Middle Dimson. The dressing floors were near the river bank, where a stamps engine house and stack stand today in dense undergrowth near the old tramway track, together with some extensive dumps.

## HAWKMOOR
D.     1852–1916
L.     ½ mile N of Gunnislake SX435726
M/O.  3,559 tons copper; 44 tons tin; 4 tons wolfram
S.     The mine lies on the small peninsula that forms the west bank of the river near Gunnislake New Bridge. There are some extensive dumps near the river bank, and the walls and masonry of a building that once supported a water wheel.

## OKEL TOR
D.     1848–1887
L.     ½ mile E of Calstock SX444689
M/O.  13,281 tons copper; 5,790 tons arsenic; 226 tons tin; 13,370 tons pyrites; small amounts of lead
S.     Okel Tor's remains are scattered over the valley side opposite to Gawton Mine and the Rumleigh brick and arsenic works, whose site is still marked by a tall, conspicuous stack. Two large pumping engine houses stand on the sett, although both are in a dilapidated condition and wreathed in ivy. The crumbling walls of a third engine house can also be located. Three stacks survive, the stump of the arsenic stack near the railway line being formerly connected by a flue to the calciners below, which are also now in ruins.

## SOUTH ZION and WHEAL ZION

D.    1849–1858

L.    ½ mile NW of Calstock SX431696

M/O.  812 tons copper

S.    A small copper producer that still exhibits two chimney stacks in a field slightly east of the railway line.

## WHEAL EDWARD and WHEAL ARTHUR

D.    1830–1885

L.    ¾ mile NW of Calstock SX429699

M/O.  19,400 tons copper; 156 tons tin; 101 tons arsenic

S.    Although adjoining the Wheal Zion sett, this mine was far more productive, as can be seen from the still surviving burrows, again east of the railway. Two chimney stacks also stand on the site.

## EAST CALSTOCK CONSOLS

D.    1822–1890

L.    ¾ mile NW of Calstock SX427701

M/O.  3,422 tons copper; 44 tons tin; 29 tons lead; 25 tons arsenic; 4,722 tons arsenical pyrites

S.    A small, very ruinous engine house and two decaying stacks are situated near the incline of the derelict East Cornwall mineral railway line.

## COTHELE CONSOLS (DANESCOMBE MINE)

D.    1880–1887

L.    1 mile W of Calstock SX423692

M/O.  72 tons copper; 323 tons arsenic

S.    The still-roofed pumping engine house of this small copper producer was restored in 1981. Nearby is the crusher house and a tall stack. All three buildings are situated in the wooded depths of the Danescombe Valley. A large adit leading into the hillside near the engine house can still be entered.

# The Tamar Valley — Devon (including Bere Alston Peninsula)

## DEVON GREAT UNITED

D.      1883–1909

L.      ½ mile NE of Latchley SX414739

M/O.  1,690 tons copper; 55 tons tin; 250 tons pyrites; 350 tons mispickel; 296 tons arsenic

S.      Lying adjacent to the immensely rich Devon Great Consols, this mine is identifiable by a mountainous dump near the river bank bordering Grenoven Wood. In the wood itself is a ruined ivy-covered stack and some crumbling masonry.

## DEVON GREAT CONSOLS

D.      1844–1901, re-worked in the 1920's.

L.      Blanchdown Plantation, 1¼ miles N of Gunnislake SX426733

M/O.  763,573 tons copper; 71,770 tons refined arsenic

S.      Considering that this was once Europe's premier copper producer, very few buildings remain on the site since its closure, the most notable being the 80 ft. high stack on the Wheal Josiah sett, dating from the 1920 re-working. In the vicinity of this chimney are the extensive and complex remains of arsenic production for which the mine became famous — mountainous and fairly poisonous dumps of burnt arsenic soot, ruined and pillaged calciners and flues, old out-buildings, water wheel pits and the dried-out beds of treatment ponds. One only has to walk along any of the numerous tracks winding through the woods to experience the aura of past mining activity — acres of disturbed land, fenced shafts, streams and pits stained with ochre. Along the footpath skirting the river bank from SX427725 to Devon United Mine, the portals of several levels can be seen, but most of these are flooded and in a state of collapse. The course of the mine's great leat also runs roughly parallel with the path, terminating near the demolished weir near Latchley. At the Lower Copper Works, where work continued into the 1940's on treating the waste tips of Wheal Fanny, there are the remains of old settling ponds, wooden launders and ochrous streams emptying into the meadow adjoining the river bank at SX428727. Part of the mine's railway can also be traced on the southern perimeters of Blanchdown Wood.

## BEDFORD UNITED

D.     1845–1909

L.     A short distance N of Gunnislake Bridge SX436725

M/O.  65,950 tons copper; 12,444 tons mispickel; 16 tons wolfram; 25 tons tin

S.     A cavernous system of levels on the Marquis Lode has its portal adjacent to the riverside footpath. The entrance is accessible, but the inner recesses are flooded. Old burrows are in the vicinity of Gulworthy Farm, the site of the original workings.

## SOUTH BEDFORD and EAST GUNNISLAKE

D.     1854–1873

L.     $\frac{1}{4}$ mile SE of Gunnislake Bridge SX435719

M/O.  5,200 tons copper; 2 tons tin

S.     A chimney stack wreathed in ivy can be found in Hatch Wood, south of the lodge and to the left of the footpath. Several levels belonging to this small group penetrate the steep hillside, and the entrances to these adjoin both the path and the river bank.

## GAWTON

D.     1846–1902

L.     $1\frac{1}{4}$ miles N of Bere Alston SX452687

M/O.  21,876 tons copper; 15,650 tons arsenic; 3,000 tons mispickel; 1,435 tons pyrites; 22 tons tin

S.     The tall, leaning chimney stack of Gawton Mine, standing on the edge of the valley north of Great Gawton Farm, is a familier landmark in the Tamar area. A massively constructed flue, still intact, connects this stack to the remains of the arsenic treatment buildings above the river near Gawton Quay. Three engine houses and an attendant stack lie in the woods halfway up the valley side, with considerable waste tips and tailings with more ruined masonry both here and lower down beside the river bank.

## BUTTSPILL (TAMAR VALLEY)

D.     1870–1886

L.     $\frac{3}{4}$ mile NW of Bere Alston SX438678

M/O.  95 tons lead; 6,508 oz silver; 710 tons fluorspar; 20 tons pyrites

S.     The ivy-covered shell of the engine house stands in dense undergrowth at the southern end of Buttspill Wood. Several shafts, treacherously obscured by bracken, and some scattered dumps are to be found adjacent to the stream flowing into the river below the engine house.

## SOUTH WARD
D.     1835–1876
L.     1¼ miles W of Bere Alston SX427678
M/O.  130 tons lead; 390 oz silver
S.     The engine house of this small lead mine has now been converted to the present-day farmhouse. The foundations over which the flatrods passed to the engine shaft (now a filled-in depression) are still visible in the grounds of Ward Farm.

## NORTH HOOE (TAMAR CONSOLS)
D.     1842–1906
L.     1½ miles SW of Bere Alston SX427661
M/O.  1,200 tons lead
S.     A large pumping engine house stands at the northern end of the small wood adjoining North Hooe Farm. Nearby is the old miners' dry. Two shafts are still open, with a burrow of some considerable size on the river bank.

## SOUTH HOOE
D.     1835–1882
L.     1¾ miles SW of Bere Alston SX425656
M/O.  14,640 tons lead; 326,300 oz silver; 780 tons fluorspar
S.     The mine's counthouse, with a distinctive bay window, stands on the site in good condition. Nearby are three walls of a small engine house. Two adits and a large dump can be located on the river bank at low water.

## SOUTH TAMAR CONSOLS
D.     1817–1860
L.     1¼ miles NW of Bere Ferrers SX437645
M/O.  7,140 tons lead; 262,470 oz silver; 350 tons fluorspar
S.     A prominent chimney stack partly wreathed in ivy overlooks the Tamar on high ground near Weirquay. The main adit is adjacent to the road below the stack and can be explored in dry weather.

## LOCKRIDGE (GOLDSTREET)

D. 1840–1861
L. $\frac{1}{2}$ mile W of Bere Alston SX439665
M/O. (as part of the EAST TAMAR CONSOLS group): 2,580 tons lead; 19,530 oz silver; 1,400 tons fluorspar
S. The conspicuous chimney stack of this mine, with ornamented brickwork showing false window openings in the topmost portion, stands in a wood near the railway line at Lockridge Bridge.

# The Tavy Valley

Unlike the Tamar Valley, which for much of it's length is fairly easy to explore, the Tavy's gorge-like slopes, in some places rising to over 300 ft. above the river, can prove an obstacle if one is planning to survey the few mining remains left in this isolated area. Steep overgrown tracks are the order of the day, some plunging into impenetrable woodland and disappearing altogether off the O/S maps. It is, however, still possible, although difficult, to walk the length of the valley from Bere Ferrers to Double Waters, making a few diversions on route.

## LOPWELL (WHEAL MARISTOW)

D. Early 1800's
L. $1\frac{1}{2}$ miles NE of Bere Ferrers SX471649
M/O. No records — lead
S. The lichen covered and decaying remains of the pumping engine house are perched above the Tavy south of Lopwell Dam. The adit has its entrance in a low bank at the back of this relic, whilst the shaft, flooded and hidden by undergrowth, is dangerous to approach. Nothing now remains of the mine's dressing floors which were formerly situated near the river bank.

## WOOD MINE

D. 1850–1861
L. $2\frac{1}{2}$ miles NE of Bere Ferrers SX478663
M/O. No records — silver and lead
S. No workings now exist in Great Whiterock Wood, which today forms part of a forestry conifer plantation. There is, however, an old men's level and dump in Rhodes Wood near the stream

flowing into the river at SX476658, although this is particularly difficult to locate.

## DENHAM BRIDGE MINE
D.     1851–1860
L.     1 mile W of Buckland Monachorum SX476681
M/O.  7 tons copper
S.     A leat and the foundation walls of a water wheel pit are near the river bank due north of the bridge. The portal of the main adit, now flooded, is at the foot of the hill in Skithead Wood.

## LADY BERTHA, EAST LADY BERTHA and SOUTH LADY BERTHA
D.     1858–1894
L.     $1\frac{1}{4}$ miles NW of Buckland Monachorum SX472688
M/O.  8,300 tons copper; some arsenic
S.     This group of old mines worked on the east bank of the river. Only a few overgrown mounds exist at South Lady Bertha (SX478682). The other two mines have waste tips, walls and ruined flues near the site of the now demolished suspension bridge, and a miners' dry stands in a field west of Balstone Farm.

## TAVY CONSOLS
D.     1850–1891
L.     $1\frac{1}{2}$ miles NW of Buckland Monachorum SX469688
M/O.  5,000 tons copper; 3,500 tons mispickel; quantities of arsenic
S.     The workings of this, the richest of the Tavy Valley Mines, lie directly opposite Lady Bertha Mine. Encroaching woodland has hidden most of the dumps and ruined furnaces from view, and the only substantial structure on the site are the massive walls of the mine's main water wheel pit, constructed of dressed granite blocks and partly filled with ochrous water.

## LITTLE DUKE (NORTH TAVY)
D.     1824–1860, re-worked 1907–1927
L.     $\frac{1}{2}$ mile N of Tavy Consols Mine SX471695
M/O.  100 tons copper; some arsenic and tin
S.     A large shaft dump can be located adjacent to the derelict Tavistock railway line in Blackmoorham Wood. Old caved-in

gunnises and levels can also be traced down the precipitous wooded slopes to Tavy Consols by the river bank.

Dir. A less arduous route to this mine and Tavy Consols, with the added attraction of some splendid scenery, is to take the Bere Alston road from Gunnislake. At the road junction marked on the O/S map as 'orestocks' (SX462697) proceed down the track signposted 'Tavistock Woodlands' for nearly $\frac{1}{2}$ mile. This eventually leads to a bridge crossing the rail track, with fine views over the valley. An overgrown path drops down to the right onto the line. Walk south until the embankment levels out and gives access to the woods. Little Duke's workings are in a clearing beside the track and can easily be reached by negotiating a gap in the embankment.

## BULLER AND BERTHA

D.     circa 1860's
L.     $\frac{1}{4}$ mile N of Buckland Monachorum SX487696
M/O.   No records — copper and tin
S.     A large dump and a walled shaft lie in a corner of a field adjoining Downlane Plantation, near Alston. The base walls of a dry still exist on the site.

# Tavistock — Okehampton

## COLLACOMBE DOWN MINE

D.     1856–1885
L.     3 miles NW of Tavistock SX434772
M/O.   8,000 tons copper
S.     The massively constructed bob wall of the engine house stands amidst extensive waste tips near Collacombe Farm and the crossroads to Lamerton.

## WHEAL FANNY (CRANDFORD)

D.     1822–1868
L.     $\frac{1}{4}$ mile SE of Bridestowe SX521883
M/O.   No records — lead
S.     The ivy-covered ruins of the bob wall and some dumps exist on the site, a short distance south east of Leawood House, although undergrowth now makes it difficult to locate these workings.

## SOURTON DOWN CONSOLS (ALICE MINE)

D.    1845–1854
L.    2¾ miles NE of Bridestowe SX542915
M/O.  No records — copper
S.    A small granite stack is still standing in a field near the junction of the A30/A386 roads, on Sourton Down, in the grounds of Minehouse Farm.

## RAMSLEY

D.    1858–1909
L.    1 mile SE of Sticklepath SX651931
M/O.  9,788 tons copper
S.    The extensive dumps of this mine are on the left of the A30 road that descends the steep hill into South Zeal, and also cover the valley side near the road to Throwleigh. The most conspicuous feature is the surviving chimney stack standing above the dumps, with the remains of a dressing plant nearby.

## WHEAL BETSY (NORTH WHEAL FRIENDSHIP)

D.    1820–1877
L.    1½ miles N of Mary Tavy SX511814
M/O.  5,000 tons lead; 60,000 oz silver

Plate 30:  *Wheal Betsy*

83

S.  The pumping engine house on Blackdown, east of the Tavistock–Okehampton road, was restored by the National Trust in 1972 and is therefore in a fine state of preservation despite the ominous bend in the stack. There are some very extensive workings on both sides of the Cholwell Brook in the direction of Kingsett. The slatey dumps scattered over Gibbet Hill on the opposite side of the road are the result of unsuccessful trials for tin dating from the 1870's.

## WHEAL FRIENDSHIP

D.  1800–1909, re-worked 1913–1925
L.  $\frac{1}{4}$ mile SE of Mary Tavy SX506794
M/O.  155,000 tons copper; 14,700 tons arsenic; 1,120 tons lead; 5,000 tons pyrites; quantities of tin
S.  The widespread workings of this prosperous mine extend both sides of the road leading into the village from Peter Tavy, particularly on the eastern side of the Cholwell Brook. Here can be seen the remains of the arsenic treatment plant, with some of the most striking condensing chambers, ovens and flues left in the county. This includes the massive flue leading to the demolished Brenton's stack, and another cast-iron flue used for refining. Old walls, trackways and leats, and some huge dumps, abound in this area.

## DEVON UNITED MINES

D.  1820–1884, re-opened 1905–1922
L.  $\frac{3}{4}$ mile E of Mary Tavy SX513788
M/O.  14,497 tons copper; 1,472 tons arsenic; 370 tons tin
S.  The remains of this group are on the east bank of the Tavy, best reached by taking the track north from the metal footbridge (SX510785) towards High Tor. Traces of calciners, flues and other masonry connected with the treatment of arsenic can be located, although encroaching undergrowth makes exploration of this site difficult. Several shafts still remain open. The large dumps near the bridge belong to the South Devon part of the sett.

## THE WALKHAM VALLEY

L.  $2\frac{1}{4}$ miles SE of Tavistock SX477699 – SX495705
S.  The valley is included here because of the numerous old

84

buildings found along the northern bank of the river, most of which housed water wheels and stamps utilised by the many smaller mines that worked the valley sides for their mineral content, and also exploited lodes on West Down, the high plateau overlooking the valley. Most of these relics, including a well preserved chimney stack, can be seen from the bottom of the trackway descending West Down (SX486703) to Grenofen Bridge, and a short distance beyond. Opposite the bridge, an array of shafts, pits and opencuts scarring the steep hillside marks the sett of POLDICE, also titled the WALKHAM MINE (SX491708). This was an unsuccessful venture that produced a few tons of lead, copper and tin from 1865 to 1890. Near the site of the now demolished viaduct are the scattered remains of WEST SORTRIDGE CONSOLS, or the GEM MINE. This operated from 1855—1872, and was re-worked in the 1880's with no results. Apart from a cavernous system of stopes and levels at SX493706, in Sticklepath Wood, only a few walls and opencuts remain hidden amongst dense woodland on the valley side. Further east, near the car park at Bedford Bridge, a few grassed-over burrows and a filled-in shaft are all that remain of WHEAL FRANCO, also called WHEAL ROBERT. The mine was active over a wide area along the south bank of the Walkham, producing 10,000 tons of copper from 1825-1870. The dumps were treated in 1875, but the mine was abandoned soon after.

## RIXHILL AND ANDERTON (TAVISTOCK UNITED)
D.      1849-1889
L.      1 mile S of Tavistock SX482723
M/O.  530 tons tin
S.      Three shafts belonging to this mine, now filled-in depressions surrounded by fencing, can be seen in a field east of the road from Rixhill to Lower Brook. Of Anderton Mine, virtually nothing now exists except for a few pits and excavations in the small wood bordering the farm of the same name.

## EAST CREBOR (EAST CROWNDALE)
D.      1852-1881
L.      1 mile S of Tavistock SX478727
M/O.  730 tons copper; 33 tons mispickel

S.      One flooded shaft is situated near the bank of the Tavy, and several grassed-over burrows lie in the surrounding fields, with a few old walls.

## DEVON AND COURTNEY CONSOLS
d.       1852–1879

L.       $1\frac{1}{2}$ miles S of Tavistock SX472717

M/O.  1,780 tons copper

S.      A few dumps remain on the outskirts of Lower and Higher Tor, together with a shaft and the base walls of a stack. Two other shafts and traces of old gunnises can be located further west in Birch Wood.